The Reed Handbook
of Common
New Zealand
Insects

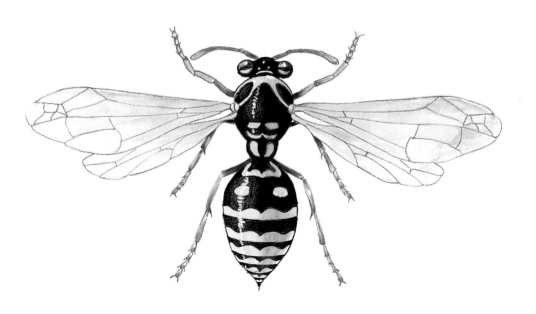

Annette Walker
Illustrations by Geoffrey Cox
and Eric Heath

REED

Acknowledgements

I gratefully acknowledge the expert advice of my colleagues in the New Zealand Arthropod Collection of Landcare, particularly Jo Berry, Robert Hoare and Richard Leschen. At the Landcare laboratory in Nelson I would like to thank John Dugdale, Jacqueline Beggs and Richard Toft. Ian McLellan's advice as an entomologist and a trout fisherman was invaluable, and an old fishing companion, Alec Kerr, assisted in sorting out some confusion with angling terms. My special thanks to numerous local friends and colleagues who have either drawn my attention to points of interest or brought me specimens for identification.

Published by Reed Books, a division of Reed Publishing (NZ) Ltd, 39 Rawene Rd, Birkenhead, Auckland. Associated companies, branches and representatives throughout the world. Website: www.reed.co.nz

ISBN 0 7900 0718 5
First published 1983/1984 as *Common Insects 1* and *Common Insects 2*.
This edition revised and updated 2000

Designed by Sharon Whitaker

Printed in Singapore

Contents

Insects in the bush

Introduction

This handbook is intended for the inquisitive observer of any age as a very general introduction to some of the common insects found in New Zealand — those that are likely to be noticed because of their conspicuous appearance, their bothersome behaviour or because they are pests. Unless otherwise stated, the insects mentioned are found throughout New Zealand.

It has been estimated that there are at least 20,000 species of insects in New Zealand and probably 90 percent of them are found nowhere else (that is, they are endemic to New Zealand). This gives New Zealand a very special status and our unique insect fauna is renowned throughout the world.

Most of these insects are found only in native habitats, especially in bush. Some are as ancient as the tuatara and, although less well known, are just as special. Some flightless species are very rare and under threat of extinction. They survive only in restricted areas of bush and as their habitat diminishes so do their numbers. Others, such as the giant weta, were once common on the mainland, but since the introduction of rats, mice and other predators, they have become restricted to some small offshore islands where they are isolated from their enemies. Like many of our endemic birds, these remarkable New Zealand insects have a very tenuous grip on survival. The preservation of their remaining natural habitats is essential for their continued existence.

What do insects eat?

Insects eat an astonishing variety of foods. The vegetable garden is where insect feeding is often most obvious, with grubs boring into tomatoes or chewing cabbage leaves. In the flower garden too caterpillars chew notches in leaves, and leave the gardener bewildered as to where the culprits lie. They hide during the day from birds and other predators and come out at night to feed.

As well as insects with 'chewing' mouthparts there are others with 'sucking' mouthparts. The effects of their feeding are less obvious but just as damaging to plants. Aphids, for instance, prefer young plant shoots, damage to which is not noticed until later when twisted leaves appear.

Many insects, such as the Lemon Tree Borer, conceal themselves by chewing inside fleshy stems or wood, and their feeding is noticed only when stems collapse or branches suddenly die. Other insects live under the ground, feeding on plant roots. The Grass Grub is one of these and the damage to pasture or lawn becomes obvious only when brown patches of dying grass appear.

Some insects eat one another, and this can be used to our advantage when an insect can be encouraged to attack a pest. There are also many inconspicuous insects helping to break down decaying animal and vegetable rubbish.

Inside the house, caterpillars eat carpets and beetles quietly chew their way through furniture. Weevils invariably find their way into stored flour or rice, and ants and cockroaches clean up any scraps left lying around. Booklice and silverfish feed on minute bits of decay, mouldy old books being a favourite food. If there are pets, their associated fleas will, given the opportunity, feed on human blood.

Whether we like it or not, insects are associated with our lives day and night, inside the home as well as outside.

Introduced and native insect pests

Some of the earliest introductions of insect pests into New Zealand were probably with Captain Cook's ships that carried cockroaches in stored food, and bed-bugs and fleas on the sailors. Later, as settlement and trading expanded, insects were brought in unintentionally with hay, soil on plants, timber and domestic animals, and pests such as blow flies, wood borers and animal parasites soon became established.

More recent and notable arrivals have included the White Butterfly, which appeared in 1929 at Napier, probably brought in with vegetables carried on a ship. The German Wasp arrived in 1944 and is another example that many New Zealanders have cause to regret, for this insect gave us our first encounter with a really unpleasant stinging insect. By comparison the bites or stings of sand flies, mosquitoes and bees are a nuisance but generally tolerable.

Insects in their native country are usually kept in check by a wide range of biological factors. For instance, in Europe severe winters keep wasp populations at a low level, while in our relatively mild climate they can thrive all the year round. Similarly, natural enemies like bacteria, viruses and parasites are often not introduced along with the pest, so sudden population explosions of the pest may occur.

We also have native insect pests. In their original habitat, where associated natural enemies are also present, these insects usually remain unnoticed. But when they spread into modified habitats many of the checks and balances that natural enemies provide are left behind. For instance, the Grass Grub has adapted well to the modified environment provided by farm pasture but its natural enemies need the diversity of its original native scrub habitat. Hence the Grass Grub, free of its natural controlling factors, has become a major pest.

Quarantine officers at all ports of entry into New Zealand are vigilant for potential pests that are brought in unwittingly by travellers on snippets of plants or food. A recent example is the White Spotted Tussock Moth that arrived in 1996. An immediate eradication programme was instigated and it has not been seen since. Some insects can travel great distances by themselves and several moth pests have arrived from Australia assisted by strong winds. An example is the Sod Webworm, which was first noticed in the late 1980s but was not seen again until 1999 and has now become a pest in some parts of Northland.

Natural enemies of insects

Insects have a wide range of natural enemies. The more obvious examples are birds, lizards, rats and mice, but there are many others of their own kind. Some, like ladybirds, are predators that attack and eat other insects; others are parasites that usually live inside their insect host. Many flies and wasps are internal parasites of other insects and may attack any stage of the insect's life cycle. The Whitespotted Ichneumonid, for instance, lays an egg in a newly formed pupa then the larva eats the contents of the pupa and emerges later by chewing its way out.

The term 'biological control' is used to describe human manipulation of these natural enemies to control insect pests. For example, the White Butterfly was brought under reasonable control when its associated parasites, which it had left behind in Europe, were successfully introduced into New Zealand. One of these parasites is a tiny wasp that lays its eggs in the caterpillar. Hundreds of wasp larvae can develop in one caterpillar, eating its internal parts but leaving the vital organs until last. The parasites eat their way out through their host's skin and spin tiny cocoons over the remains of their victim — a gruesome story but a very effective way of naturally controlling White Butterfly.

Insects are also attacked by fungi, and a particularly spectacular example is the *Cordyceps* fungus which attacks Porina caterpillars. The fungus transforms its host into a mummified 'vegetable caterpillar' and then produces a stalk or 'fruiting body' which pushes its way up the old Porina burrow and protrudes above ground to release its spores. Bacterial diseases are also used for biological control; for example, the bacterium commonly known as 'Bt' (*Bacillus thurin-giensis*) is used to control caterpillar pests.

Viruses also attack insects. For instance, if too many caterpillars are kept crowded in a cage, or populations reach high densities naturally, caterpillars often appear flaccid and are found hanging over a branch or lying dead and bloated. If this delicate skin is touched, often a foul smelling soup-like fluid will ooze out of the caterpillar's body.

Collecting insects

Insects are found in a wide variety of habitats. Likely places are under stones or dead wood, but one should always make sure that these are replaced in their original position and that the collecting site is disturbed as little as possible. Don't be a 'vacuum cleaner' — leave some specimens behind. One carefully handled specimen, correctly labelled, is more worthwhile than hundreds of damaged specimens with no data about where they were collected.

Making an insect collection is an absorbing and inexpensive pastime. For catching flying insects, a round angler's landing net (with a cone-shaped gauze bag about 80 cm long replacing the fish net) is ideal. Insects are swept up into the bag and then transferred to a 'killing jar'; a 250 g preserving jar with a tight-sealing lid and a 1 cm layer of plaster of Paris on the bottom is a suitable container. A few drops of ethyl acetate are added before use. This chemical can be obtained from a chemist's shop, but be *very careful* not to inhale the poisonous fumes and to keep the chemical away from plastic. Add some strips of tissue paper to the jar to absorb excess moisture and keep it away from the sun. Alternatively, live insects can be killed immediately by storing them in a deep freeze for a few hours.

Dead specimens can be either pinned or glued to a piece of stiff cardboard. If this is done within 24 hours the specimen is easier to spread out in a lifelike position. Finally, add a neatly printed label under the specimen, giving the locality, date, type of habitat and collector's name.

Insects are best stored in shallow drawers or wooden store boxes. The polyethylene foam packing material, 'Plastazote', is the ideal pinning base for insects. Polystyrene can be used as an alternative but it is not such a secure base for holding pins. There are insects that like to eat dead specimens and a small block of camphor held by pins in a corner of the box is the traditional, and still the best, way of keeping these pests from attacking a collection. To avoid damage to specimens by sunlight and mould, always store the collection away from light and damp, preferably on an inside wall.

Insect pets

Many insects easily adapt to a confined space and with care and attention their habits and life cycles can be closely observed. For instance, praying mantids and katydids can be kept in a large jar with a gauze top. For stick insects and crickets take a large, sturdy-cardboard box, cut large windows in the top and sides and cover with clear plastic. This cage is also very suitable for rearing caterpillars. A plastic fish tank is suitable for keeping ground beetles, earwigs or cockroaches. Wetas live in old insect holes and come out at night to feed; an artificial weta house can be constructed by boring weta-size holes (about 12 mm in diameter) in one end of a block of untreated timber. Split the block, then lash it together and either attach or hang it upside down in native vegetation in the garden. After a month or two, untie the block and hopefully you may have a specimen or two in the wood. Gibbs, in his book *New Zealand Weta* (see Further Reading), gives an excellent account of keeping wetas in captivity.

Make sure any insect cage is kept well away from direct sunlight and fresh food plants are always available — they can even be grown in a pot in the cage. A fine mist spray of water once a day keeps the plants and insects fresh. Many insects are active only at night and shelter during the day; leaves or dead wood lying on the cage floor are necessary as hiding places. Other insects such as ichneumonids and butterflies need a source of honey to feed on. A small jar filled with a solution of honey and water with a wick forced through a slot in the lid is a good feeding container but the honey solution must be renewed every few days or it will go mouldy. Clean cages are essential: when the insect cage is empty, clean it in hot soapy water to remove any bacteria or virus that might infect the next insect in the cage. Consider too that many insects can be kept in a room for a day or two outside the confines of a cage. A Praying Mantis, for instance, will find plenty of flies, and a Bag Moth will happily feed on a bunch of leaves kept in a jar of water.

Most important of all, if you tire of the insect or it seems stressed, let it go, returning it to where it was found.

A butterfly garden

The suggestion of a butterfly garden may seem a little fanciful, but it is possible to attract butterflies into a garden planted with suitable host plants and flowers. However, to be successful, ensure that no insecticide sprays are used.

Monarch Butterfly caterpillars live on the swan plant, a border of which will be quickly recognised by a female searching for somewhere to lay her eggs. Red Admiral and Yellow Admiral caterpillars breed on nettles. These may not be the most attractive garden plants but if your curiosity overrides any apprehension, a secluded corner of nettles (fenced off from children) is well worth experimenting with. A patch of ragwort will attract Magpie Moths and their Woolly Bear caterpillars, and the vegetable garden will naturally attract White Butterflies. While you may not be too popular with the neighbours, a cloud of white, fluttering butterflies over a row of unsprayed cabbages is an attractive sight.

It is also possible to attract the more elusive endemic species into gardens, especially if you live close to native bush. The Forest Ringlet, *Dodonidia helmsii*, breeds on *Gahnia* or *Chionochloa* grass and specimens may frequent gardens planted with these. Likewise, the Common Copper, *Lycaenia salustius*, may be attracted to *Muehlenbeckia*. The tiny Common Blue Butterfly is often seen fluttering over lawns planted with clover species.

Butterflies like to feed in long, tubular-shaped flowers, which are easily probed with their long, uncoiled proboscis. *Buddelja* flowers are particularly suitable, and are a sure way of attracting butterflies.

Insects and the angler

Anglers have a special interest in aquatic insects because they are eaten by trout. For instance, author Norman Marsh has recorded no less than 864 Caddisfly larvae, 70 Mayflies, 18 beetles and four Dobsonfly larvae in a 1 kg trout caught in a small limestone stream. It goes without saying that he does not mention the locality!

Fly fishers tempt trout with imitation insects called 'flies' (not to be confused with the entomologist's use of the word for the order Diptera). Sinking 'wet flies' are used to imitate underwater insect larval stages, which anglers often call 'nymphs', but this is not quite the same meaning of the word that entomologists use. They call a nymph the immature stage of an insect developing by incomplete metamorphosis (see Insect classification, page 16). Anglers also use floating 'dry flies', which are intended to imitate either the adult insects that drop onto the water from streamside vegetation, or those that emerge out of the water as newly hatched adults. The latter are especially common at dusk during warm, still, summer weather when there is frantic activity by insects hatching, mating and laying eggs. Anglers call this time the 'evening rise' as the trout rise to snap up insects, often leaping out of the water and leaving radiating ripples as they dive down again.

How an insect is named

Common insects usually have an accepted common name, often derived from their host plant (the Cabbage Tree Moth), or physical appearance (the New Zealand Praying Mantis). This may seem a reasonable way to give a name to an insect but what happens when there are two kinds of praying mantids that look very alike?

Over 200 years ago, Carl Linnaeus, a famous scientist from Sweden, developed a system of naming different kinds, or species, of plants and animals that has continued in much the same fashion to the present day. This system is used and recognised by scientists all over the world.

In very simple terms it is much like the way a first name and a surname are given to people. As an example, the New Zealand Grass Grub's scientific name is *Costelytra zealandica*. Just as a surname refers to all members of one family, the 'generic' name *Costelytra* refers to all members of a closely related group or genus. The generic name is always written first and starts with a capital letter. The second or 'specific' name, *zealandica*, is used like our first name and there can be many different species in a genus, just as there can be many brothers and sisters in one family. The specific name never has a capital letter and is often a descriptive word referring to the appearance or, as in the Grass Grub, defining the locality where it is found. The whole name is always in Latin form and is normally printed in italics.

The full insect name includes, after the generic and specific names, another name that is not printed in italics. This refers to the person who originally gave the insect its scientific name. If the insect is later shifted to a different genus from the original author's one, the author's name is given in brackets.

This name is often abbreviated. For instance, insects named by Linnaeus are indicated by 'L.' after the specific name. In many New Zealand species 'F.' follows the specific name as in the Manuka Beetle, *Pyronata festiva* (F.). This is an abbreviation of Fabricius, the scientist who named the insects collected on Captain Cook's first voyage to New Zealand in 1769.

Insect classification

Insects are classified into 29 divisions or 'Orders' and within each 'Order' there are further divisions called 'Families'. Beetles, for instance, belong to the Order Coleoptera and the Click Beetle is in the Family Elateridae. The Orders range from the most primitive wingless insects (for example the Thysanura, or silverfish) to the most highly developed social insects (the Hymenoptera, or ants, bees and wasps).

The more primitive insects have an incomplete metamorphosis or growing sequence from egg to adult. For instance, baby grass-hoppers are called nymphs, and hatch from the egg looking very much like miniature adults. These develop through successively larger but similar-looking stages by shedding their skin (moulting). There may be up to eight of these stages before the adult size is reached.

The more advanced Orders have a more complex system of development with only a few immature or larval stages that are distinctly different from the adult form. Then the larva changes or meta-morphoses into a pupa that is inactive and often encased in a protective cocoon. Finally, the pupa changes to the adult, which lays eggs to start the cycle again. This process is called a complete metamorphosis. The Monarch Butterfly is an example of an insect with this more complex system of development, passing through the several larval or caterpillar stages followed by a pupa or chrysalis, before emerging as an adult butterfly.

Most of the major Orders are represented in the section **Insects in the field and garden**. First come insects from the more primitive Orders: the praying mantids, katydids, crickets, locusts, cockroaches and earwigs. They are followed by the Hemiptera or true bugs with sucking mouthparts. Then come the more advanced Orders with complete metamorphoses: the beetles or Coleoptera that have hard wing cases (elytra) covering the abdomen, the Diptera or flies with two wings, the Lepidoptera or moths and butterflies, and finally the Hymenoptera that have four wings and include the bees, wasps and ants.

A guide to some of the common insects found in New Zealand

This illustrative guide is intended as a simple key to the identification of some of the common insects found in New Zealand and is a summary of the insects described in this book. The guide represents most of the major Orders likely to be noticed. Where the larval stage is distinctive or common it has also been illustrated.

Mayflies Order: Ephemeroptera 	**Cockroaches** Order: Blattodea
Damselflies Order: Odonata Suborder: Zygoptera 	**Praying Mantids** Order: Mantodea
Dragonflies Order: Odonata Suborder: Anisoptera 	**Earwigs** Order: Dermaptera
Stoneflies Order: Plecoptera 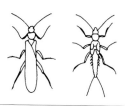	**Katydids** Order: Orthoptera Family: Tettigoniidae 

Weta
Order: Orthoptera
Family: Stenopelmatidae

Stick insects
Order: Phasmatodea

Cave Weta
Order: Orthoptera
Family: Rhaphidophoridae

Leaf hoppers
Order: Hemiptera
Family: Ricaniidae (several
other families also)

Grasshoppers
Order: Orthoptera
Families: Tettigoniidae and
Acrididae

Cicadas
Order: Hemiptera
Family: Cicadidae

Crickets
Order: Orthoptera
Family: Gryllidae

Aphids
Order: Hemiptera
Family: Aphididae

Pentatomid bugs
Order: Hemiptera
Family: Pentatomidae

Tiger beetles
Order: Coleoptera
Family: Carabidae

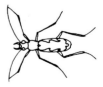

Backswimmers
Order: Hemiptera
Family: Notonectidae

Water beetles
Order: Coleoptera
Family: Dytiscidae

Water Boatmen
Order: Hemiptera
Family: Corixidae

Staphylinid or Rove beetles
Order: Coleoptera
Family: Staphylinidae

Dobsonflies
Order: Megaloptera
Family: Lucanidae

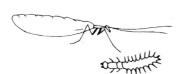

Stag beetles
Order: Coleoptera

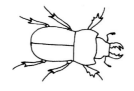

Lacewings or Antlions
Order: Neuroptera

Chafer beetles
Order: Coleoptera
Family: Scarabaeidae

Ground beetles
Order: Coleoptera
Family: Carabidae

Click beetles
Order: Coleoptera
Family: Elateridae

Mosquitoes
Order: Diptera
Family: Culicidae

Ladybird beetles
Order: Coleoptera
Family: Coccinellidae

Soldier flies
Order: Diptera
Family: Stratiomyidae

Sand flies
Order: Diptera
Family: Simulidae

Longhorn beetles
Order: Coleoptera
Family: Cerambycidae

Robber flies
Order: Diptera
Family: Asilidae

Weevils
Order: Coleoptera
Family: Curculionidae

Hoverflies
Order: Diptera
Family: Syrphidae

Crane flies
Order: Diptera
Family: Tipulidae

Muscid flies
Order: Diptera
Family: Muscidae

Blowflies
Order: Diptera
Family: Calliphoridae

Ichneumonid wasps
Order: Hymenoptera
Family: Ichneumonidae

Tachinid flies
Order: Diptera
Family: Tachinidae

Spider wasps
Order: Hymenoptera
Family: Pompilidae

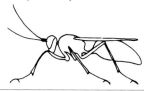

Caddisflies
Order: Trichoptera

Paper wasps
Order: Hymenoptera
Family: Vespidae

Butterflies
Order: Lepidoptera

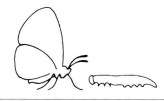

Mason wasps
Order: Hymenoptera
Family: Trypoxylidae

Moths
Order: Lepidoptera

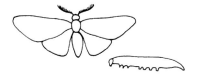

Ants
Order: Hymenoptera
Family: Formicidae

Insects
in the
field and garden

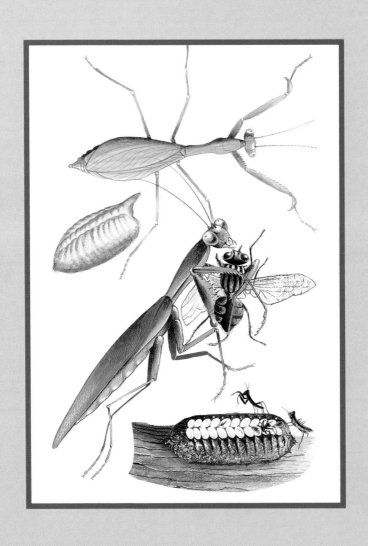

Introduction

The insects selected for this section are mainly those found in modified environments such as farms, urban gardens or houses, although some of them will also be found in other habitats.

An interesting number of Australian butterflies are swept across the Tasman Sea to New Zealand. They usually occur sporadically and provide an additional and often colourful variety of unusual species to our gardens and countryside, sometimes even establishing themselves for a year or two. These marathon flights are usually associated with unusual weather patterns and it has been estimated that, on one such occasion, it took the Blue Moon Butterfly three days to arrive, probably being initially uplifted by thermals and turbulent mixing over southern New South Wales or Victoria. This book is not the appropriate place to mention all of these unusual butterflies (see *New Zealand Butterflies Identification and Natural History* by George Gibbs under Further Reading), but the Blue Moon Butterfly is probably the most conspicuous, being up to 110 mm with black wings and large white or orange patches. They often arrive in a very battered condition and can occur in large numbers with as many as 720 specimens being recorded in 1956.

Katydid / Kikipounamu
Caedicia simplex (Walker)
Order: ORTHOPTERA
Family: Tettigoniidae

The Katydid's quiet, hesitant 'zip, zip' song is often heard in gardens on still summer evenings. It is produced by the Katydid rubbing its wings together, and the characteristic sound is delightfully suggested by the Katydid's other name of Scissorsnip. The Maori name, Kikipounamu, means 'faint' (sound) and 'green'. This Katydid is also found in Australia.

Katydids are friendly insects. They are common in gardens but are difficult to find; not only does their colour blend in with their surroundings but the wings also have a leaf-like shape and texture. Katydids normally have an ungainly 'slow motion' gait, but if disturbed they will fly or jump away with their long, powerful hind legs. They feed on foliage and spend much time grooming themselves like a cat.

The females have a short, curved ovipositor and usually lay their black, wedge-shaped eggs in rows on plants during autumn. Adults and smaller wingless nymphs actively feed at night and are found throughout most of the year.

Adult body length: 40 mm.

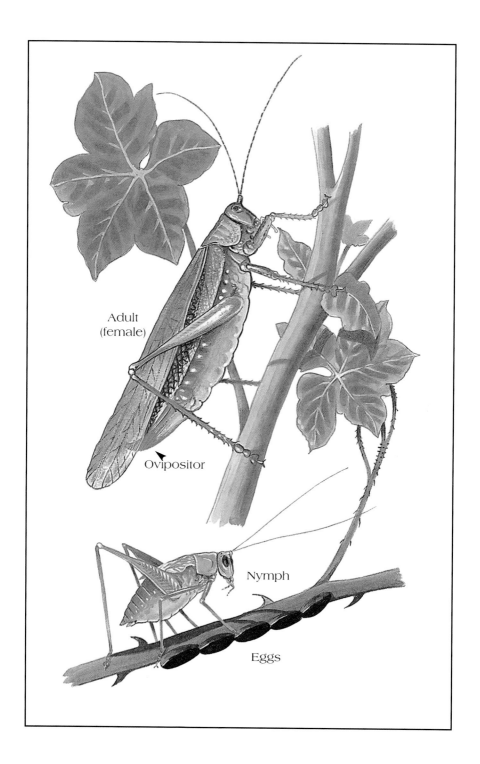

Adult
(female)

Ovipositor

Nymph

Eggs

Black Field Cricket
Teleogryilus commodus (Walker)
Order: ORTHOPTERA
Family: Gryllidae

Late summer and autumn evenings are often filled with the wavering chirp of these crickets. This strident mating song is produced by the male rubbing its wings together.

At night, Black Field Crickets creep out from their shelters in cracks, or under stones, to feed on foliage. In some areas of the North Island they cause severe damage to pasture; even a moderate population can consume as much grass as several sheep per hectare. Adults can fly but when disturbed they usually jump with their powerful hind legs and scuttle back to shelter. Often in late summer, if their natural habitat is disturbed, for instance by the mowing of grass or a sudden burst of rain, they will seek shelter inside houses.

Females have a short, pointed ovipositor, which they use for inserting their white, cigar-shaped eggs about 1 cm deep in damp ground. The young crickets hatch in spring, looking like miniature adults but without fully developed wings. They finally become adults after nine moults.

Black Field Crickets are found throughout the North Island and in the warmer regions of the South Island, as well as in Australia.

Adult body length: 20 mm.

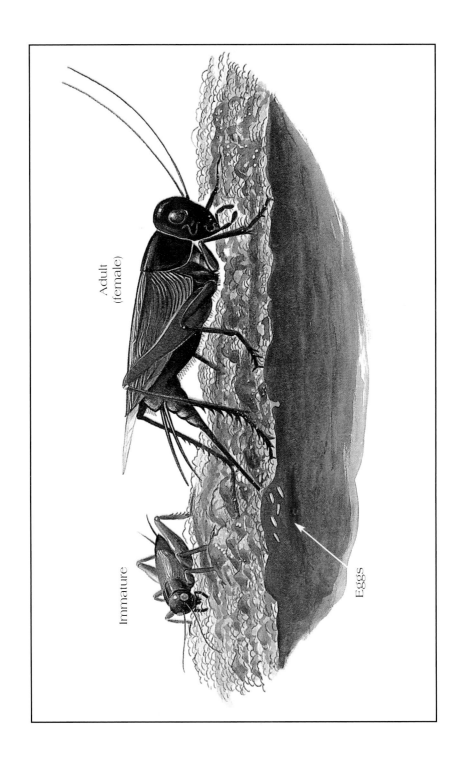

Adult
(female)

Immature

Eggs

29

Migratory Locust / Kapakapa / Rangataua

Locusta migratoria (L.)
Order: ORTHOPTERA
Family: Acrididae

The Migratory Locust is exactly the same species as the plague locust of Africa and has probably been in New Zealand since before European settlement. Fortunately, here it does not develop into the gregarious form whereby millions of nymphs and adults congregate to feed and cause vast devastation to crops.

The Migratory Locust is found in lowland, uncultivated grass habitats in the North Island and as far south as Mid-Canterbury. On hot, autumn days the large adults, with their powerful jumping hind legs, are very active, and if disturbed they take off for a short, clattering flight, making a crash landing a few metres away. Few adults survive the winter but large numbers of eggs remain in the ground and hatch in the spring. The wingless, smaller nymphs feed on vegetation, developing through a series of moults until they are mature with fully developed wings.

Adult body length variable from 30–60 mm.

European Earwig
Forficula auricularia L.
Order: DERMAPTERA
Family: Forficulidae

Earwigs have short wing cases, usually with a pair of filmy wings neatly folded underneath, but they rarely fly. When spread out, these have an ear-like shape, which gives rise to the old common name 'ear-wing', later corrupted to 'ear-wig'. Contrary to one belief the name has nothing to do with crawling into the human ear.

Earwigs are not particularly choosy about what they eat, but the European Earwig can be found eating pollen in flowers or feeding in stone fruit — and is often encountered with distaste after finishing a particularly good garden peach. Adults and their young are easily recognised by their pincer-shaped projections on the end of the abdomen. In some species these are used to catch prey, which is then crushed and eaten.

In autumn the female excavates a cavity in the ground and lays up to 30 globular eggs. Unlike most insects, she then stays with the eggs until they hatch in the spring. The nymphs look like miniature adults and the first to hatch devour any smaller nymphs and remaining eggs. They have four moults and take 14–15 weeks to mature.

Adult body length: 10 mm.

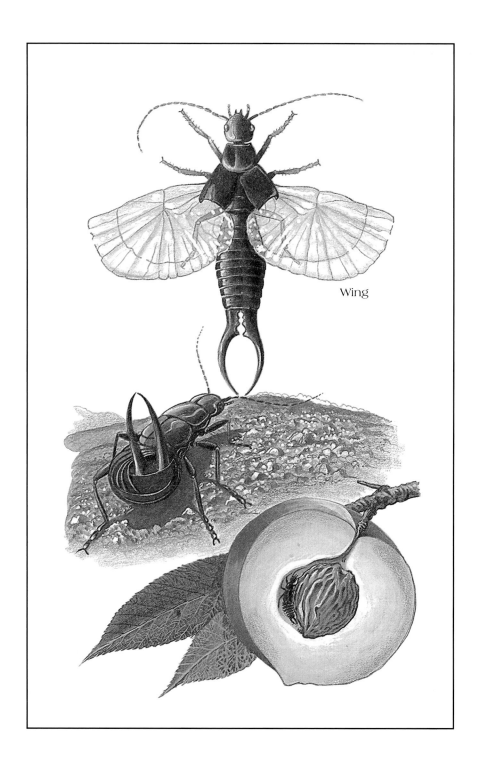

Wing

33

Gisborne Cockroach
Drymaplaneta semivitta (Walker)
Order: BLATTODEA
Family: Blattidae

The conspicuous Gisborne Cockroach lives mainly outside, usually in wood piles, but it is also found inside — perhaps brought in with firewood. It was first found in New Zealand at Tauranga in 1954, probably introduced with log shipments from Western Australia. It is now common in the Gisborne area and has spread as far as Auckland and Palmerston North.

Adult body length: 25 mm.

German Cockroach
Blattella germanica (L.)
Order: BLATTODEA
Family: Blattellidae

The German Cockroach probably arrived in New Zealand with Cook's first ship in 1769. Its flattened shape enables it to squeeze into cracks in walls or cupboards during the day and at night it comes out of hiding to search for scraps of food. Usually they are seen only if the kitchen light is suddenly switched on, when startled cockroaches scurry for cover. Females are sometimes seen lugging around their rather cumbersome, purse-shaped egg capsules. These take some time to detach and the eggs inside are also slow to hatch. When the tiny cockroaches emerge they look similar to the adult but have reduced wings.

Adult body length: 15 mm.

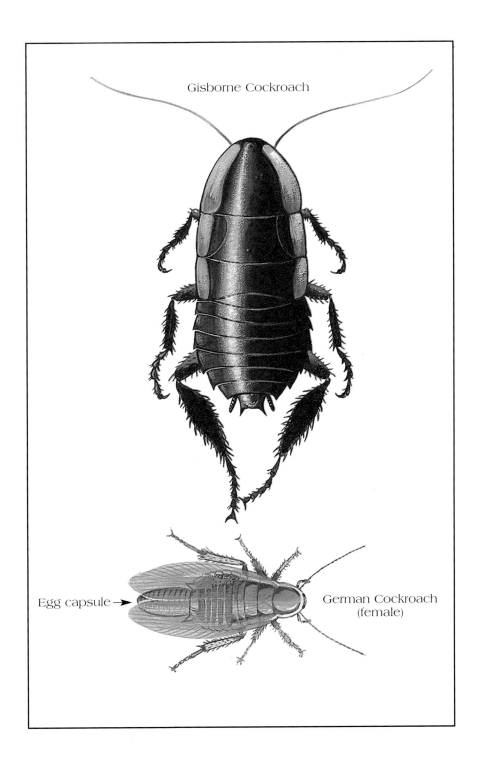

Gisborne Cockroach

Egg capsule →

German Cockroach
(female)

Praying Mantids
Order: MANTODEA
Family: Mantidae

Praying Mantids make excellent pets and their behaviour is fascinating to watch: while they can run very rapidly when provoked, most of the time their camouflaged body sways like a leaf in the wind. The rotating head with bulging eyes searches for a victim and the front legs are poised ready to pounce on any suitable insect that comes within reach. The female mantis sometimes even eats its own mate. Once the victim is seized and clamped between the spiny legs it is delicately eaten, and after the meal the mantis carefully cleans its legs and spines.

Springbok Mantis
Miomantis caffra Saussure

A smaller, more delicate-looking South African species called the Springbok Mantis, was first discovered in Auckland in 1978 where it is particularly common in gardens but it has been collected as far north as Kaitaia. It can easily be distinguished from its New Zealand relative by the narrow 'neck' behind the front legs and the characteristic foamy-looking egg cluster.

Adult body length: 40 mm.

New Zealand Praying Mantis
Orthodera novaezealandiae (Colenso)

Mantis is a Greek name meaning 'prophet' or 'divine', derived from the habit of tucking their long powerful front legs together in a prayer-like manner. In late summer the New Zealand Praying Mantis is common in gardens throughout New Zealand, the females fat and heavy with eggs. These are laid in zipper-like cases cemented on to branches or fences. In the spring the tiny mantis hatches and struggles out of its cell, looking like a miniature wingless adult. After a series of moults during the summer it finally becomes an adult.

This larger species of mantis was, for a long time, thought to be Australian but more recently it was recognised as a distinct New Zealand species.

Adult body length: 40 mm.

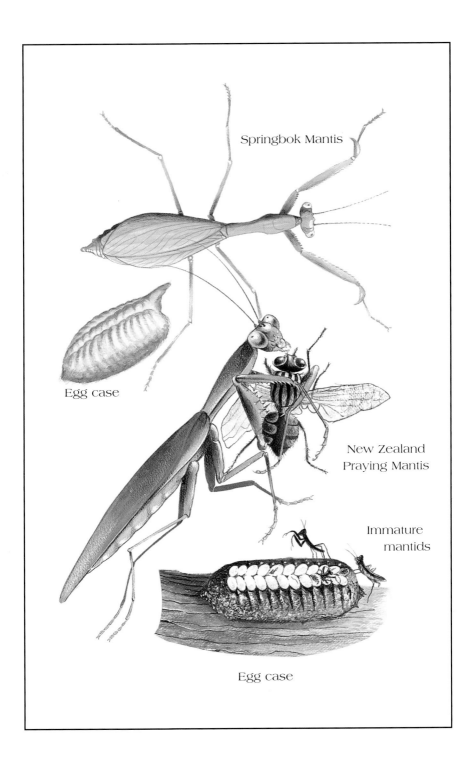

Springbok Mantis

Egg case

New Zealand
Praying Mantis

Immature
mantids

Egg case

Passionvine Hopper
Scolypopa australis (Walker)
Order: HEMIPTERA
Family: Ricaniidae

The Passionvine Hopper arrived from Australia over 100 years ago. It is now a common garden pest in the North Island and in Nelson and Marlborough. Although the adult is moth-like in appearance, it does not belong to the order Lepidoptera but to the 'true bugs' called Hemiptera. The female inserts her eggs into plant stems, pushing aside the damaged fibres. Eggs hatch in the spring as tiny, wingless hoppers, easily recognised by their tufted abdomen.

Adults and nymphs feed on plant juices, often congregating in long rows on the plant stems and leaves. Their sweet, sticky secretion called honeydew spreads over the plant and sooty mould soon grows on it. The poisonous native plant tutu (*Coriaria arborea*) is attacked by the hopper and this can cause a serious problem for beekeepers. Bees gather the honeydew and, although not poisonous to the bee, the honey produced from it is a danger to humans. At certain times of the year honey production is banned in some areas of New Zealand.

Adult body length with wings folded: 10 mm.

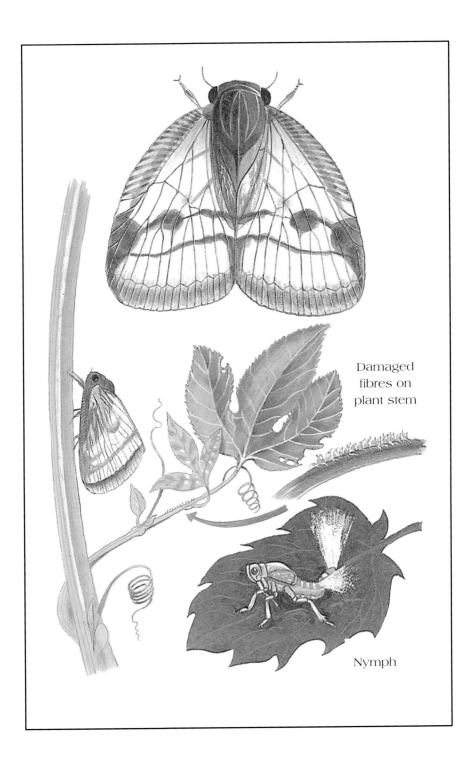

Damaged
fibres on
plant stem

Nymph

39

Clapping Cicada / Kihikihi wawa
Amphipsalta cingulata (F.)
Order: HEMIPTERA
Family: Cicadidae

New Zealand has many native species of cicada and, unlike the rest of the world, many species live high in the mountains. Each has its characteristic song, but the Clapping Cicada is the largest and noisiest. In late summer the massed song of the males can be deafening and the descriptive Maori name, Kihikihi wawa, means 'roaring like heavy rain'. The sound is produced by a complicated pair of voice chambers on the abdomen as well as by clapping the wings.

The nymphs (Fig. A) are rather grotesque creatures that spend their entire life underground sucking the sap from tree roots. They have characteristically enlarged front legs adapted for digging and grasping. In summer, fully grown nymphs make their way to the surface and anchor themselves to bark. The outer skin splits open down the back and the adult cicada emerges, leaving behind an empty case.

Female cicadas have a powerful ovipositor and thrust their eggs deeply into plant tissues, often causing damage. Eggs lie dormant over winter, hatch in spring, and the tiny nymphs drop and crawl into the ground, probably not to see daylight again for several years.

Adult body length with wings folded: 40–45 mm.

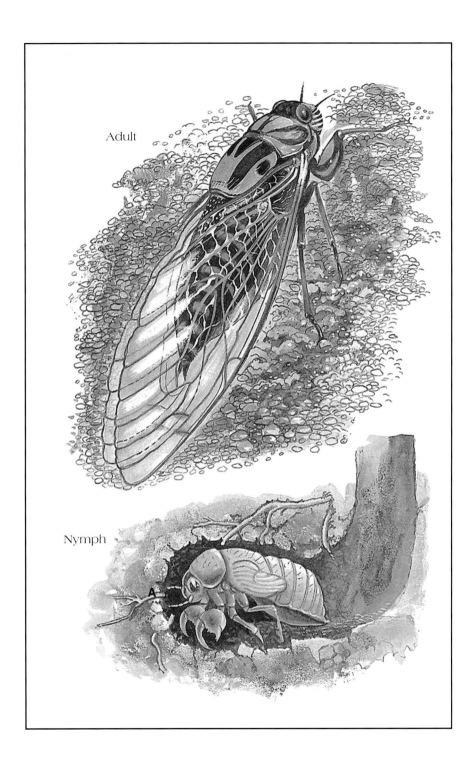

Adult

Nymph

A

41

Cabbage Aphid

Brevicoryne brassicae (L.)
Order: HEMIPTERA
Family: Aphididae

Aphids are persistent pests in home gardens, damaging young plant shoots by sucking the juices with their sharp proboscis. They are also carriers or 'vectors' for many of the viruses that cause plant diseases. Aphids vary in colour from green to black, and have the appearance of something out of science fiction, with spindly legs and a pair of erect tubes or cornicles on the abdomen.

The powdery-looking Cabbage Aphid is only one of nearly 100 endemic and introduced aphids found in New Zealand. Like many other species it is parthenogenetic (the female reproduces without mating) and viviparous (the eggs develop inside the female and she produces live young). In spring, winged females fly to young cabbage seedlings and establish new colonies. These produce successive generations of wingless aphids throughout the summer until autumn, when winged females are again produced. These then fly off to spend the winter on other crops like turnips, which they often infect with turnip virus. The mummified aphids that are often found in colonies have been parasitised by a minute wasp.

Adult body length: 1–2 mm.

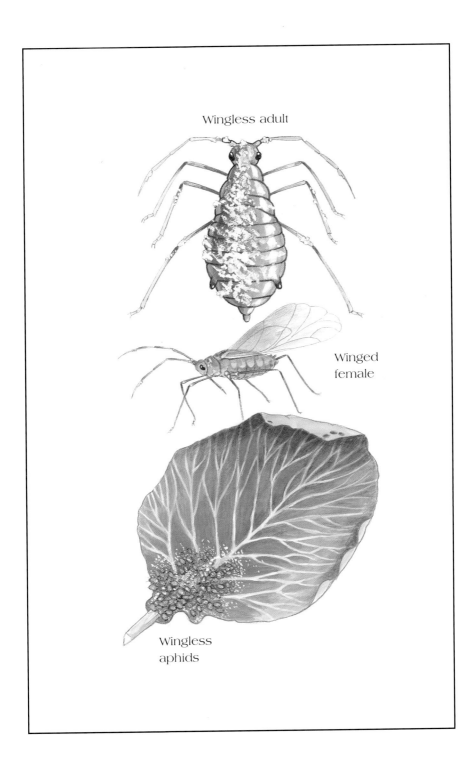

Wingless adult

Winged female

Wingless aphids

Green Vegetable Bug
Nezara viridula (L.)
Order: HEMIPTERA
Family: Pentatomidae

This garden pest is found all around the world. It was first recorded in New Zealand at New Plymouth in 1944 and is now established throughout the North Island and in Nelson and Marlborough. There is a very similar native species, *Glaucias amyoti*, which lacks the three spots on the back and is not considered a pest.

The Green Vegetable Bug feeds by piercing plant tissue with its sharp, pointed mouthparts and then sucking the juices. The resulting injury to the plant causes, for example, deformed beans and corky growth on fruit. Adults lay beautiful egg clusters under leaves. The smaller immature stages are quite different from the adult but feed in the same way and cause similar damage. Several generations can develop in a year depending on the climate.

When disturbed, the adult Green Vegetable Bug secretes a foul-smelling brown liquid, which is an effective defence mechanism repellent to most predators.

Adult body length: 15 mm.

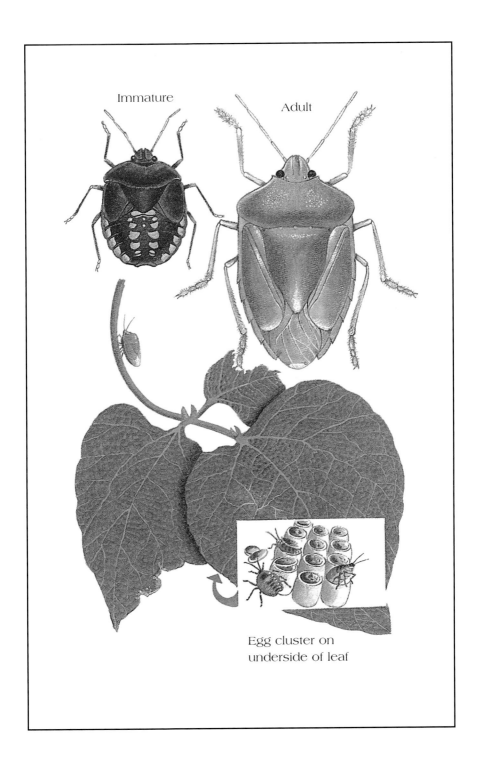

Immature

Adult

Egg cluster on
underside of leaf

45

Cosmopolitan Ground Beetle

Laemostenus complanatus (Dejena)
Order: COLEOPTERA
Family: Carabidae

There are about 400 different species of ground beetles, or Carabids, found in New Zealand. They range in size from 2 mm to 35 mm but all are black or metallic-looking, with hard wing cases or elytra and bead-like antennae. They are predators and use their long, agile legs and prominent jaws to chase and seize other insects. The larger ground beetles can inflict a painful bite if handled roughly and some also give off a foul-smelling defensive secretion.

The Cosmopolitan Ground Beetle is often found in old wood piles or under stones in gardens; it has membranous wings that are normally tucked out of sight under the elytra, and because it is a strong flier it has spread naturally throughout the world. On the other hand, many endemic species are flightless (see Carabid Beetles, page 110) and hence are restricted to particular localities. These species are very vulnerable to extinction if their natural environment is either modified or destroyed.

Adult body length: 15 mm.

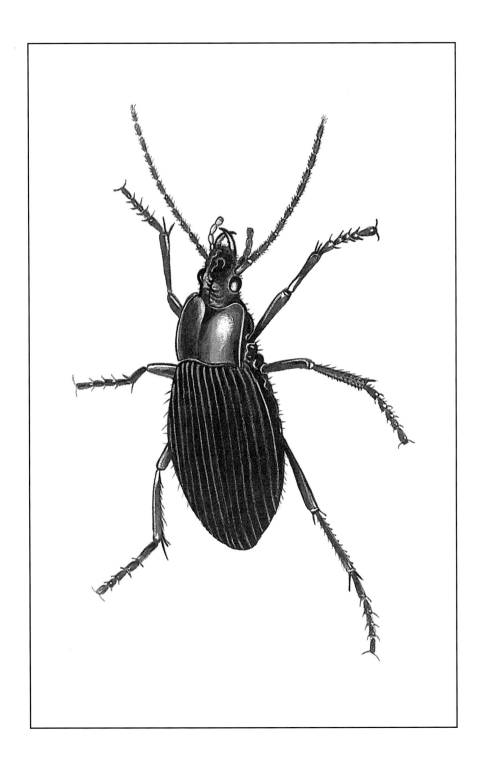

Devil's Coachhorse Beetle
Creophilus oculatus (F.)
Order: COLEOPTERA
Family: Staphylinidae

In ancient Europe, the Devil's Coachhorse Beetle was surrounded by superstition. The Celts, for instance, believed that it was the devil that 'eats the bodies of sinners', so the association was perhaps not surprising as the beetle lives in decaying vegetable matter or under dead animals. Also according to folklore, farmers carried them at harvest time for good luck.

Both the adults and larvae are predators that feed on other insects. The adults have strong, sickle-shaped jaws with which they tear apart fly maggots or pupae and suck out their juices. If disturbed, the beetle curls up its flexible abdomen and produces a secretion smelling like rotten fish from glands near the tip of its body.

The Devil's Coachhorse Beetle found in New Zealand and Australia has an orange spot behind each eye. Despite its short wing cases it has large membranous wings underneath and is a strong flier. Adults are attracted to lights and are found throughout the year.

Adult body length variable from 13–20 mm.

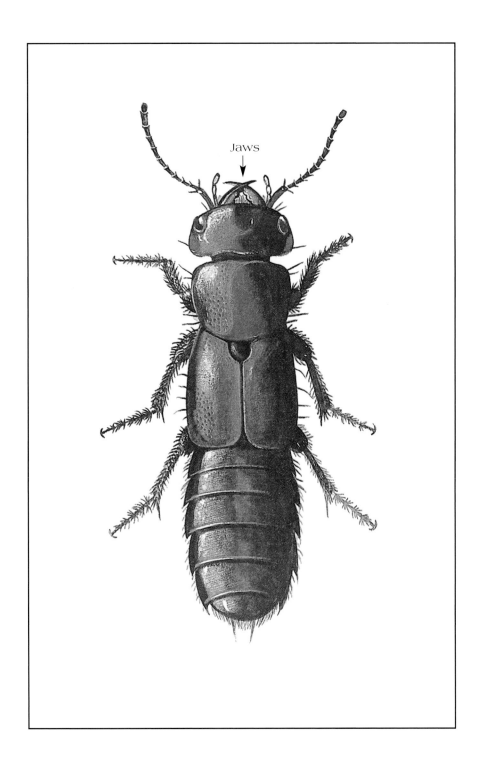

Jaws

Grass Grub / Tutaeruru

Costelytra zealandica (White)
Order: COLEOPTERA
Family: Scarabaeidae

The native Grass Grub is found throughout New Zealand and is considered to be one of New Zealand's major pasture pests. However, there are probably over 100 other species of scarab beetles in New Zealand (see pages 116 and 118), many looking very similar to the common Grass Grub. With a few exceptions they are also found only in New Zealand.

In its natural open-grassland habitat, Grass Grub numbers are regulated by parasites and predators, but with the advent of farming, the Grass Grub has moved into improved pasture, leaving most of its natural enemies behind.

Eggs are laid in clusters in the soil in summer. They hatch in about two weeks and the larvae feed on grass roots until spring. Heavily infested pasture develops patchy brown areas, and in severe cases the turf 'mat' is chewed loose from the soil and can be rolled back to expose hundreds of fat grubs lying on the soil surface. In spring the mature grubs burrow further down and construct cells in which they pupate.

Adults emerge from their pupae in November, and in infested areas mass flights occur at dusk on warm, still nights, when the air is filled with the soft buzzing of slowly flying beetles. Later the beetles often congregate and feed in huge numbers on nearby trees and shrubs, which may be severely defoliated.

Adult body length: 10 mm.

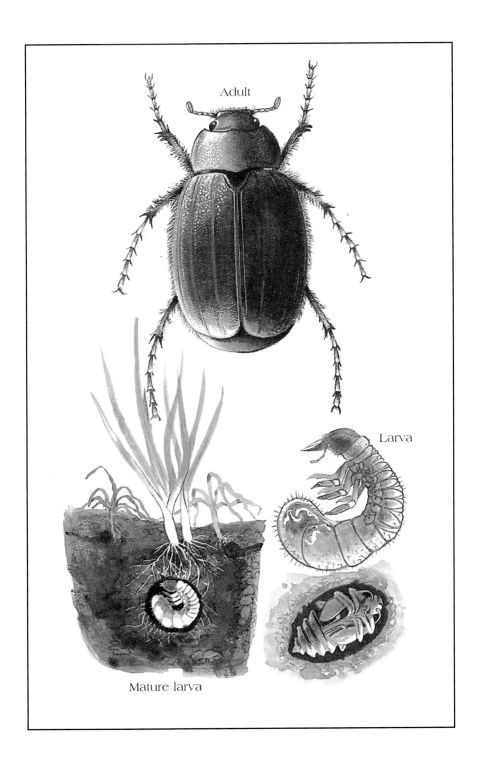

Adult

Larva

Mature larva

Click Beetle / Pasture Wireworm

Conoderus exsul Sharp
Order: COLEOPTERA
Family: Elateridae

Click Beetles are attracted to lights and often fly into houses on summer evenings. There they usually attract attention by clicking like a ballpoint pen as they try to right themselves. The click is produced by a cunning mechanism situated underneath the beetle. A blunt spine on one body segment is wedged into a trough-shaped cavity in the adjoining segment. As the beetle arches its back, the spine bends and flicks out of the groove, throwing the beetle into the air and making the click as it goes. In contrast to its robust body, the Click Beetle's legs are spidery. When it is disturbed these legs are quickly tucked in and the beetle 'plays dead' to fool predators.

The larvae of Click Beetles are called Wireworms and live in the soil, feeding on plant roots and small soil animals during the winter. They pupate and emerge as adult beetles in the spring. There are many native Click Beetles found in New Zealand but the country of origin of this common species is uncertain.

Adult body length variable from 10–15 mm.

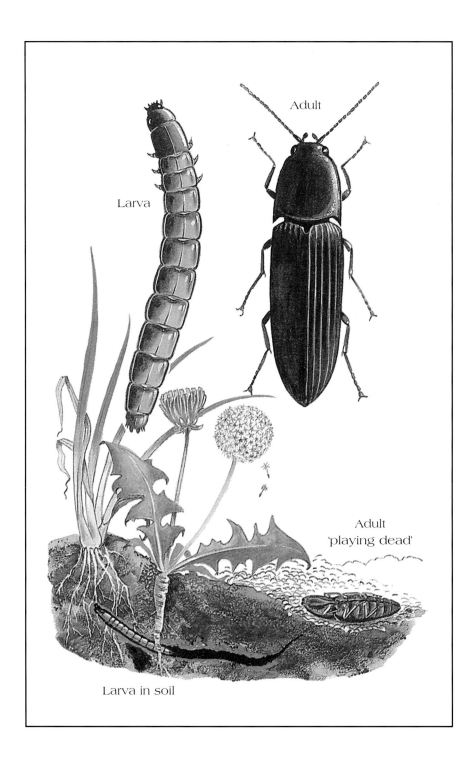

Larva

Adult

Adult
'playing dead'

Larva in soil

Ladybirds
Order: COLEOPTERA
Family: Coccinellidae

Ladybirds are beneficial in controlling some insect pests. Both adult and larval stages feed on aphids, mites and scale insects. The hemispherical adults are strong fliers but their wings are usually neatly folded under their hard outer wing cases or elytra. By contrast, the larvae are wingless, rather ugly, wrinkled creatures which move around slowly as they feed on their helpless victims. The adults hibernate during winter, often sheltering together in small clusters under bark. In the spring the females lay their eggs close to aphid colonies that provide a convenient food source for the larvae when they hatch.

Elevenspotted Ladybird
Coccinella undecimpunctata L.

The Elevenspotted Ladybird and the Steelblue Ladybird are only two of many species of native and introduced ladybirds in New Zealand. The Elevenspotted Ladybird is found in gardens and orchards and was deliberately introduced into New Zealand from England in 1874. It has the distinction of probably being the first deliberate introduction into New Zealand of an insect for biological control purposes.

Adult body length: 5 mm.

Steelblue Ladybird
Halmus chalybeus (Boisduval)

The conspicuous Steelblue Ladybird is from Australia and is often seen on citrus tree leaves, where it feeds on minute scale insects.

Adult body length: 5 mm.

Larva

Elevenspotted
Ladybird
(adult)

Steelblue Ladybird
(adult)

Red-winged Lycid Beetle

Porrostoma rufipenne (F.)
Order: COLEOPTERA
Family: Lycidae

The first encounter with this beautiful beetle for most people is on hot sunny days when it is seen struggling to keep aloft. One's eye is caught by the red flash of its soft forewings (elytra) as it flies relatively close to the ground in a rather blundering, haphazard fashion. Unfortunately, when the beetle dies, the bright red usually turns to orange.

This beetle is the only representative of the Lycidae family in New Zealand and somehow it has made its way to this country from Australia. Other members of the family are thought to be mimics of other insects that are distasteful to birds and the bright colour is a warning signal to potential predators.

Although the Red-winged Lycid Beetle has been in New Zealand for many years, it is only now appearing in greater numbers. Beetles neither sting nor bite and are often found on garden flowers where they feed on pollen and nectar. Very little seems to be known about its life cycle but the larvae are reported to live under the bark of logs. Beetles are found throughout the North Island as well as around the Nelson district.

Adult body length: 9–19 mm.

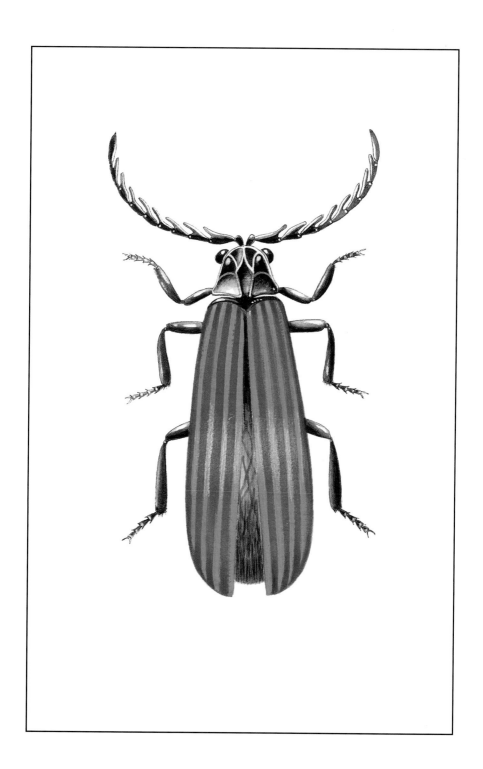

Lemon Tree Borer

Oemona hirta (F.)
Order: COLEOPTERA
Family: Cerambycidae

This is a native wood-boring beetle, found in both native and introduced trees throughout New Zealand. As its common name suggests, it favours citrus trees and can be a serious pest in citrus orchards in the North Island. The larvae bore tunnels through live stems and branches, often weakening them to such an extent that they break off. The Lemon Tree Borer is only one of a number of conspicuous longhorn or cerambycid beetles (see pages 120 and 122) found in New Zealand, characterised by their long antennae.

The long, wrinkled larvae spend a year feeding in their narrow tunnels, and the fine sawdust or frass which they produce can often be seen caught in cobwebs in the trees or scattered on the ground beneath. The larvae pupate in their tunnels and emerge as adult beetles in the spring. The beetles vary in size, depending on how well they have fed as larvae. If handled roughly the beetle may 'stridulate', rasping together file-like structures on its thorax to produce a squeaky noise.

Adult body length variable from 17–30 mm.

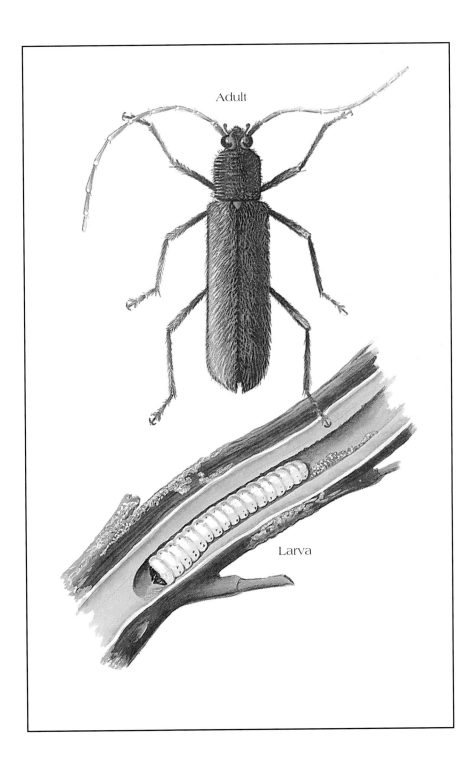

Adult

Larva

Crane Flies
Order: DIPTERA
Family: Tipulidae

New Zealand has hundreds of species of Crane flies or Tipulids. They come in a wide range of sizes and colours and only a small proportion of them have been given scientific names. They are also called Daddy-long-legs and are understandably confused with the Daddy-long-leg spider that lives in ceilings.

On summer evenings crane flies are attracted to lights and sometimes cause concern with their blundering flight round a room. However, they are quite harmless and if you contemplate catching one to let go outside, handle it carefully as its long and fragile legs break off easily.

Adults live for a very short time — only long enough to mate and for the female to lay eggs. Very little is known about the biology of most species; some are predators, others live in rotten wood. One common Crane Fly is found in damp pasture, and has larvae called Leather-jackets that can cause damage by eating the grass roots.

Adult wingspan variable from 10–40 mm across.

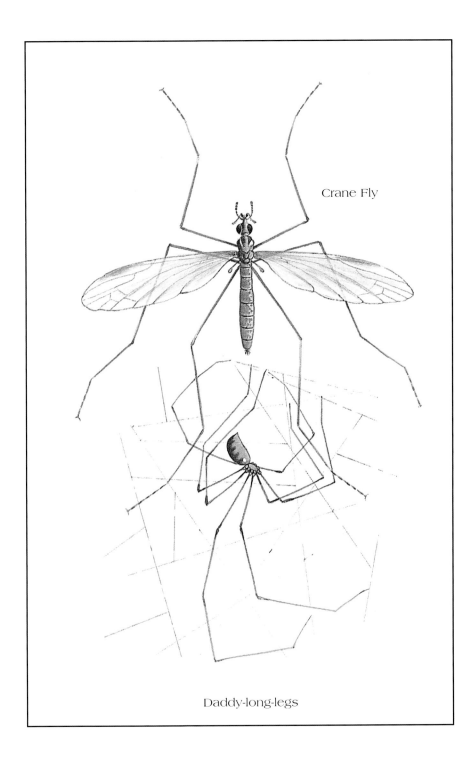

Crane Fly

Daddy-long-legs

Soldier Flies
Order: DIPTERA
Family: Stratiomyidae

A frantic buzzing on the window is what usually draws attention to the Soldier Fly. It may sound like a bee but it has only two wings and is therefore quite harmless. The flat, wrinkled maggots live in compost heaps and probably occur throughout the country.

American Soldier Fly
Hermetia illucens (L.)

The American Soldier Fly has spread to many places round the world, including Australia and the Pacific, and was first noticed in New Zealand in Auckland in 1956. It is found during summer and is distinguished by its dusky wings.

Adult body length with wings folded: 20 mm.

Garden Soldier Fly
Exaireta spinigera (Wiedemann)

The Garden Soldier Fly is more common than the larger American Soldier Fly. Only half its wings are dusky-coloured, and adults are found all through the year. It is also found in Australia and records indicate that it has been in New Zealand certainly since 1911, but probably arrived earlier, after the advent of trading.

Adult body length with wings folded: 15 mm.

American Soldier Fly

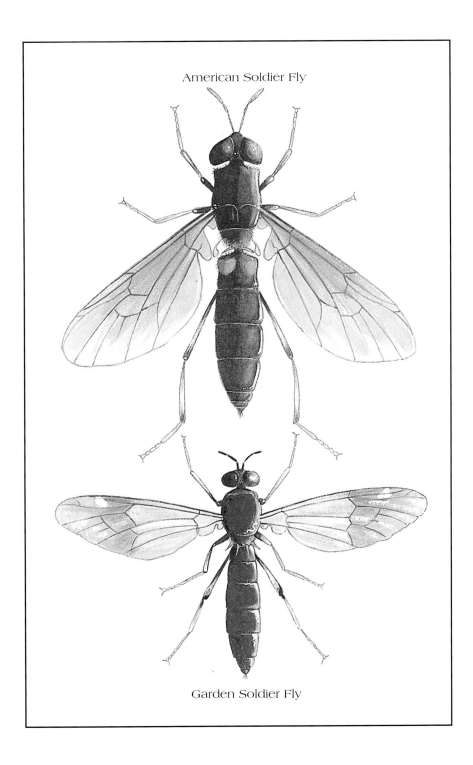

Garden Soldier Fly

Drone Fly

Eristalis tenax (L.)
Order: DIPTERA
Family: Syrphidae

To the casual observer the Drone Fly often passes unnoticed as it looks very similar to a bee. But close examination reveals that it has only two wings and is therefore a fly. The Drone Fly and the bee do, however, feed on the same flowers and compete for the same food.

Their similar appearance may in fact not be a case of mimicry, that is, those Drone Flies whose appearance mimicked that of stinging bees survived best as they evolved. Rather, it is the result of convergent evolution: both insects developing a similar structure because of their similar feeding behaviour of gathering up pollen on their hairy bodies while searching for nectar in flowers. The Drone Fly can be seen hovering and darting from flower to flower on sunny days throughout the year.

The Drone Fly is widespread throughout New Zealand and was self-introduced from the northern hemisphere, probably in its larval stage, which is a rat-tailed maggot that lives in rotten slush.

Adult body length: 15 mm.

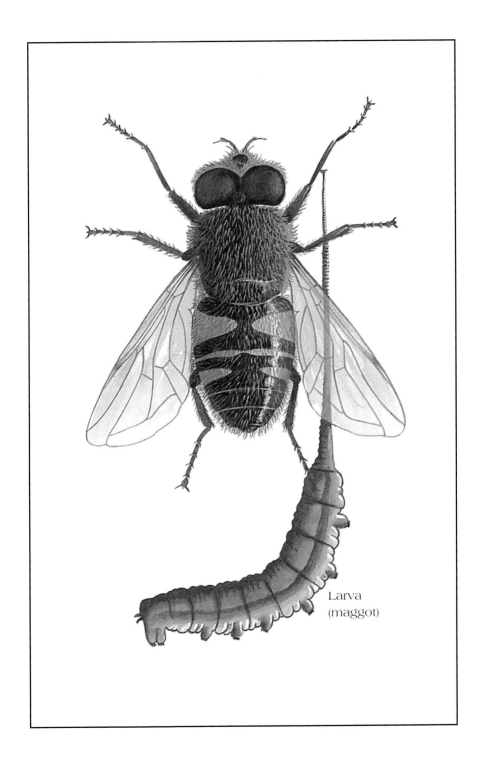

Larva
(maggot)

Blow Flies and House Flies
Order: DIPTERA

In New Zealand there are many introduced and native blow flies and house flies whose maggots feed on decaying animal and vegetable matter. Blow flies can generally be distinguished by their fat, metallic blue or green abdomen, while house flies are usually duller with a more hairy and patterned abdomen.

Stable Fly
Stomoxys calcitrans (L.)
Family: Muscidae

The Stable Fly looks very similar to the common House Fly but, instead of the House Fly's pad-like sucking mouth, it has a piercing proboscis used for biting and sucking blood. It will bite humans and is often encountered on country picnics, but usually it pesters animals in paddocks and cowsheds where the maggots live in silage or dung.

Adult body length: 8 mm.

European Blow Fly
Calliphora vicina Robineau-Desvoidy
Family: Calliphoridae

The European Blow Fly is often attracted by cooking smells inside houses, where it has an annoying habit of zooming around erratically. There is a similar, but larger, native blow fly that is more common in bush habitats and also causes annoyance inside houses (see page 132).

Adult body length variable from 5–12 mm.

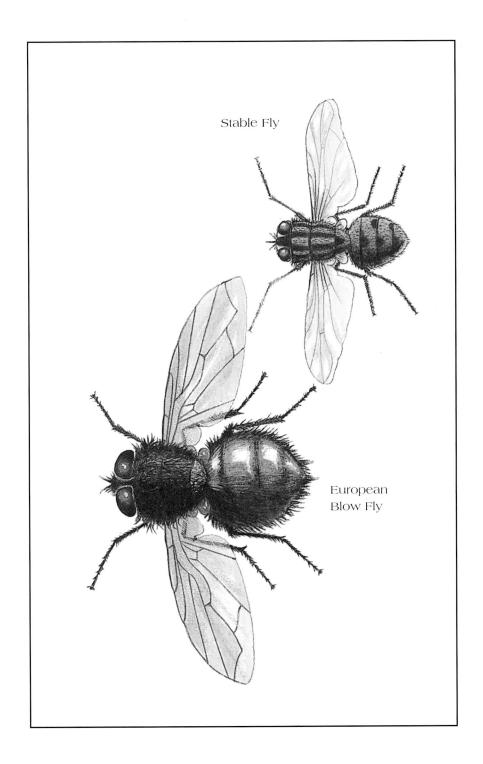

Stable Fly

European
Blow Fly

Porina Moths
Wiseana species
Order: LEPIDOPTERA
Family: Hepialidae

There are many species of native Porina moths in New Zealand, several of which are major pasture pests. They are difficult to identify exactly, but all can generally be recognised by their short antennae and a characteristic resting position with the wings folded like a roof over the body.

In their original native grassland habitat, Porina moths are controlled by parasites and predators, but these natural enemies have unfortunately not followed them into farmland. Porina caterpillars live underground in tunnels during the day and at night come out to feed on grass and other foliage above ground. Often there are so many that their grazing leaves bare patches in the pasture. When touched, the flabby caterpillars have a curious wriggle and secrete a brown fluid. They grow up to 6 cm long and then pupate in their burrow. The moth emerges at dusk, leaving its empty pupal skin at the tunnel entrance. The adult life is brief, for the moth has no mouthparts for feeding. In a few evenings, however, the female can lay thousands of eggs, spraying them over the pasture like a topdressing plane.

Adult wingspan variable from 35–60 mm.

Larva

Common Bag Moth
Liothula omnivora (Fereday)
Order: LEPIDOPTERA
Family: Psychidae

The bag of this moth is both camouflage and protection for the caterpillar that lives inside. It is a native insect that feeds on both native and introduced plants. If approached quietly its fascinating behaviour can be observed: the caterpillar cautiously pokes its head out to feed, while holding on inside the bag with its hooked legs. When disturbed it quickly withdraws and shuts the top tightly. The bottom end remains open to eject faecal pellets. As the caterpillar grows it enlarges the bag with silken extensions and attaches plant fragments to the outside.

The caterpillars pupate in their bags in the spring but only the inconspicuous male moths emerge. The female has no wings and remains inside her bag, the male fertilising her through the bag's open end. She lays eggs which later hatch inside the bag and the tiny caterpillars escape through the opening.

Maori call the bag kopi, meaning 'shut', and it was sometimes used by early settlers as a plectrum for playing the autoharp. It is also referred to as the Case Moth.

Adult male wingspan: 30 mm; length of bag variable from 20–90 mm.

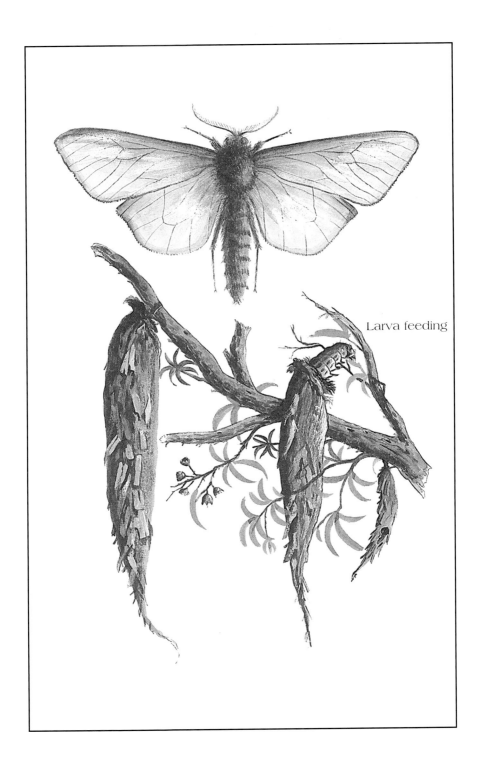

Larva feeding

White Butterfly

Pieris rapae (L.)
Order: LEPIDOPTERA
Family: Pieridae

This European butterfly first appeared in New Zealand in 1929 at
Napier, where it was probably accidentally introduced from among
vegetables carried on a ship. The butterfly spread rapidly, and with
few natural enemies to control it, soon became a serious garden
pest. Later its larval and pupal parasites were introduced from
Europe and these now generally keep White Butterfly numbers in
check.

The White Butterfly is found from early spring to autumn having
overwintered as a pupa and it usually has several generations a
year. Each female, which can be distinguished from the male by
the two pairs of spots on the forewings, lays 300–400 bullet-
shaped, yellow eggs under the leaves of cabbage or other
Brassica plants. The eggs hatch after six days and the tiny
caterpillars rapidly chew their way through the leaves, leaving
only a skeleton of veins. The velvety caterpillars have five stages
or instars. They reach a length of 30 mm before they wander off
the plant to pupate in an inconspicuous place — usually on dead
leaves or on fences. Some ten to fifteen days later the adult butterfly emerges.

Adult wingspan variable from 40–50 mm.

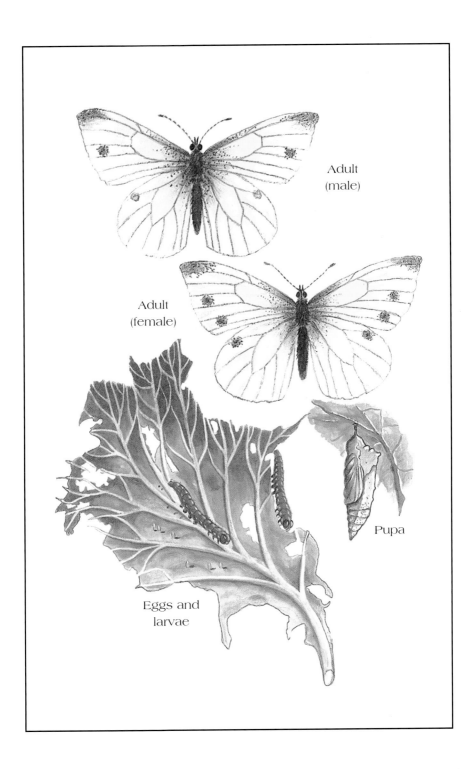

Adult
(male)

Adult
(female)

Pupa

Eggs and
larvae

Monarch Butterfly
Danaus plexippus (L.)
Order: LEPIDOPTERA
Family: Nymphalidae

Throughout summer this beautiful butterfly flies about looking for a mate and a place to lay eggs. It has been estimated that a single female can lay up to 700 individual creamy-yellow eggs before she dies. The male attracts the female by scent stored in black spots on each hind wing. Caterpillars feed on swan plants (*Asclepias physocarpa*) and have five stages or instars before they reach their full length of 55 mm. Then their voracious feeding stops abruptly and they wander off the plant, searching for a suitable site to pupate. It is fascinating to watch as they hang upside down and then suddenly shed their skin and transform into a pupa. About three weeks later the pupa darkens and soon the adult butterfly emerges.

In North America, the same Monarch Butterfly migrates each winter to warm areas like California. There, year after year, they gather in large numbers on 'butterfly trees'. Butterflies do not appear to migrate in New Zealand but they do cluster on trees in winter in Nelson, Hastings and Northland, and scientists have been tagging specimens to trace their movements.

It is uncertain exactly how or when the Monarch arrived in New Zealand. Species of swan plant do not occur naturally here, therefore it would have had to migrate more or less at the same time as its host plant. Early reports indicate that the Monarch had arrived by late last century and it has been suggested by a New Zealand author that the swan plant probably arrived independently with early sailors who used the old, fluffy seed heads of the swan plant for stuffing bedding and life jackets.

Adult wingspan variable from 70–100 mm.

Pupa

Larva
preparing
to pupate

Yellow Admiral / Kahu kowhai
Bassaris itea (F.)
Order: LEPIDOPTERA
Family: Nymphalidae

The Yellow Admiral is found in New Zealand, Australia and the Pacific and was first collected in New Zealand during Captain Cook's voyage in 1769. Although not as common as its close relative, the native Red Admiral (see page 100), it is occasionally seen gliding round gardens throughout summer. Yellow Admiral butterflies hibernate during winter and the following summer old, battered specimens can be seen struggling to keep aloft.

The male and female butterflies look very similar. The female lays her eggs on the underside of introduced nettle plants, attaching them to the nettle stings. The caterpillars also look very like Red Admiral caterpillars and pupate after reaching a length of 40 mm. Eventually the pupa darkens and a few days later an adult butterfly emerges. The pupa normally responds with a characteristic wriggle when disturbed; if it does not then this may be an indication of a sick pupa that has been parasitised by the Whitespotted Ichneumonid wasp (see page 86).

Adult wingspan: 50 mm.

Cabbage Tree Moth

Epiphryne verriculata (Felder and Rogenhofer)
Order: LEPIDOPTERA
Family: Geometridae

This native moth is rarely noticed, but its caterpillar causes conspicuous damage to cabbage trees (Ti kouka, *Cordyline australis*) all over New Zealand. The moth is an excellent example, of camouflage. During the day it rests on the underside of dead leaves with its wings flat, the lined pattern on its wings blending in perfectly with the veins of the leaf.

The female moth lays batches of eggs on the cabbage trees, and caterpillars hide inside the growing crown of the tree during the day, crawling out at night to feed. The young caterpillars feed voraciously in the centre spike, but the surface damage they cause is not revealed until later in the summer when the leaves unfurl. Older caterpillars eat characteristic holes and notches in the cabbage tree leaves. They pupate at the base of the dead leaves or in the debris under the tree.

Adult wingspan variable from 25–35 mm.

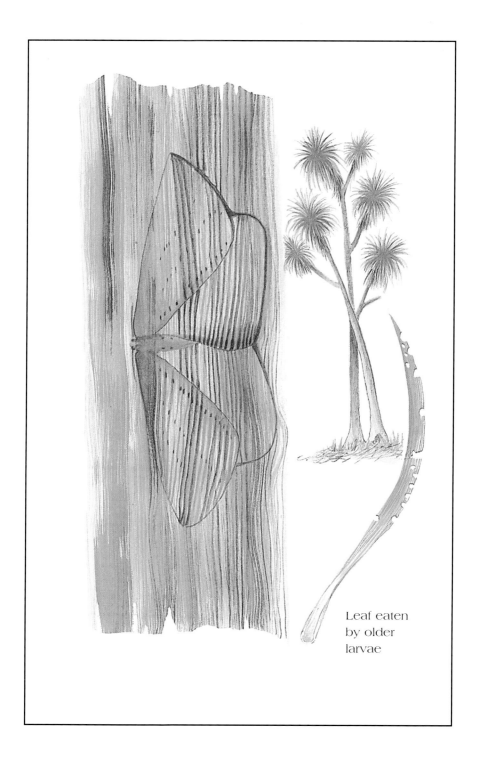

Leaf eaten
by older
larvae

Gum Emperor Moth
Antheraea eucalypti Scott
Order: LEPIDOPTERA
Family: Saturniidae

This very large, furry moth was probably an accidental introduction to New Zealand from Australia. It was first discovered in Wanganui in 1915 and is now established throughout most of the North Island and in Nelson. It flies at night in early summer, and is often attracted to lights. The male has delicate plume-like antennae that detect the scent of the female, whose antennae are more slender.

The moths have a short life; they do not feed, and live long enough only to mate and then lay eggs on eucalyptus or pepper-tree leaves. The striking appearance of the caterpillars is probably an adaptation to scare off hungry birds. They are voracious feeders, quickly reaching a length of up to 130 mm, and by the end of January they are ready to pupate. The caterpillar becomes dark and sluggish and commences to spin a sturdy, brown, silken cocoon. The pupa hibernates in this until spring when the moth emerges.

Adult wingspan variable from 100–140 mm.

Mature larva

Cocoons

Magpie Moth

Nyctemera annulata Boisduval
Order: LEPIDOPTERA
Family: Arctiidae

Unlike most other moths, the native Magpie Moth flies during the day, and is brightly coloured. This is thought to be an example of warning colouration, advertising to potential predators that it is not good to eat. The reason for this unpalatability seems to be because the caterpillars feed mainly on plants (such as ragwort) that contain poisonous chemicals called alkaloids. These protect the plant against attack by most insects, but the Magpie Moth has developed immunity to these chemicals and actually uses them for its own defence. The caterpillar stores the alkaloids, which are retained in the pupa and also in the adult moth.

The hairy caterpillars, known as Woolly Bears or Tupeke, are often seen wandering about on garden paths. Fully grown caterpillars reach a length of about 30 mm then spin a protective, web-like, silken cocoon in which to pupate, often among garden rubbish.

Adult wingspan variable from 40–45 mm.

Grapevine Moth

Phalaenodes glycinae Lewin
Order: LEPIDOPTERA
Family: Agaristidae

The Grapevine Moth is similar to the Magpie Moth. This day-flying moth self-introduced from Australia and inhabits the Auckland region. It is easily recognised by the band of yellow on the forewing.

Adult wingspan variable from 40–45 mm.

Magpie Moth

Magpie Moth larva

Grapevine Moth

Cinnabar Moth
Tyria jacobaeae (L.)
Order: LEPIDOPTERA
Family: Arctiidae

Like the Magpie and Grapevine moths, the Cinnabar Moth flies during the day. As its name implies, it is a spectacular vermilion and smoky grey colour, unlike any other moth or butterfly we have in New Zealand. This moth also feeds on ragwort and was introduced into New Zealand from England in 1929. Over the following three years, nearly 3.5 million eggs were distributed on ragwort throughout the country. However, in spite of this mammoth undertaking, the moth almost died out except in small pockets in the Wairarapa.

In early 1982, Cinnabar Moths were collected from the Wairarapa sites and reliberated throughout the country. It has now successfully re-established in several areas throughout New Zealand and is very common in the Hutt Valley, Marlborough Sounds and Nelson.

There is only one generation a year and clusters of yellow spherical eggs are laid on the underside of ragwort leaves, taking about two weeks to hatch. The caterpillars grow quickly and can be seen from about December to February. Although both the Magpie and Cinnabar Moths have bold stripes, unlike the hairy Woolly Bear caterpillars of the Magpie Moth, the caterpillars of the Cinnabar Moth are quite smooth with only a few scattered hairs.

After about one month of feeding, caterpillars wander off the ragwort and usually find a sheltered place close to the ground to pupate. They require a dry place in which to overwinter as pupae and mature caterpillars have been known to seek the shelter of stored cloths in garages in which to pupate.

The bright colours of both the moth and the caterpillar are thought to be examples of warning colouration, advertising that they are not good to eat for they store poisonous chemicals called alkaloids derived from the ragwort which they eat.

Adult body length: about 20 mm.

Adult

Eggs

Pupa

Ichneumonid Wasps
Order: HYMENOPTERA
Family: Ichneumonidae

The Dusky-winged Ichneumonid and the Whitespotted
Ichneumonid are both found in Australia and are typical of a multi-
tude of similar-looking ichneumonid wasps found in New Zealand.
They are sometimes called 'horse stingers', but their long, needle-
like 'sting' is a harmless ovipositor used only for egg laying.

Dusky-winged Ichneumonid
Lissopimpla excelsa (Costa)

The Dusky-winged Ichneumonid parasitises the soil-dwelling pupae
of Cutworm and other Noctuid moths. This is a fascinating process
to watch: the female ichneumonid's antennae quiver and tap the
ground as she searches for a pupae, and when she finds one the
quivering becomes even more excited. Then she manoeuvres her
ovipositor into position, like a drilling rig on the back of a truck, to
pierce the pupa and inject an egg into it. When the egg hatches,
the parasite larva devours the body contents of the live moth pupa
and then pupates in the empty shell. In the spring, instead of a
moth, the wasp emerges.

Adult body length variable from 10–20 mm.

Whitespotted Ichneumonid
Echthromorpha intricatoria (F.)

The Whitespotted Ichneumonid, like the Dusky-winged
Ichneumonid, parasitises pupae including those of Red and Yellow
Admiral butterflies and Magpie moths.

Adult body length variable from 10–15 mm.

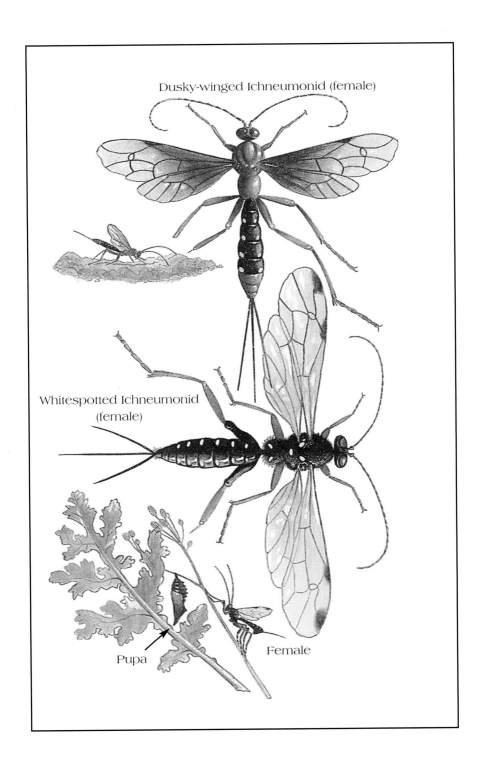

Dusky-winged Ichneumonid (female)

Whitespotted Ichneumonid (female)

Pupa

Female

87

Vespid Wasps
Order: HYMENOPTERA

During summer Vespid wasps forage for insects to feed to their developing larvae. Later, as the larvae mature, their diet changes to sugary substances — honeydew from beech trees (*Nothofagus* species) is a favourite food of the Common Wasp.

Vespid wasps chew wood and bark fibre to produce 'paper' that they mould into cells where the larvae develop. The nests are usually constructed underground with only a small entrance hole visible, but they also build nests in roofs and other sheltered places. The nests are usually deserted in winter; the workers die but the queens hibernate until spring.

German Wasp
Vespula germanica (F.)   Family: Vespidae

The German Wasp became established in New Zealand in 1944 after nests were introduced from Great Britain in cases of aeroplane parts stored at Hamilton.

German Wasps construct their nests from sound wood and have a greyish appearance. Some German Wasp nests are able to survive the winter and can reach astronomical proportions, the largest ever found was about 4 metres high and contained about four million cells.

Adult body length length variable from 15–22 mm.

Common Wasp
Vespula vulgaris (L.)   Family: Vespidae

The Common Wasp became established in New Zealand during the 1970s. Common wasps collect wood fibre from dead and rotten wood and their nests are brown. It can be distinguished from the German Wasp by the different colour patterns on the body and behind the eyes. The Common Wasp, on the whole, is darker than the German Wasp and has a dark patch behind the eye, whereas the German Wasp has an uninterrupted yellow area.

Adult body length variable from 15–22 mm.

European Tube Wasp
Ancistrocerus gazells (Panzer)   Family: Vespidae

The European Tube Wasp first appeared in Auckland in 1998 but it has now spread as far south as Otago. Although similar in appearance to the German and Common wasps, it is much smaller (about 10 mm) and does not have a vicious sting. It can be found on hot, sunny days investigating small cracks and holes where it makes a single-celled nest. The nest is provisioned with a tiny caterpillar, then sealed off with a mud lid. Later the wasp larva hatches, eats the caterpillar and emerges as an adult.

Adult body length: 10 mm.

German Wasp

Nest

Head, German Wasp

Common Wasp

Head, Common Wasp

European Tube Wasp

Polistes Wasps
Order: HYMENOPTERA
Family: Vespidae

Australian Paper Wasp
Polistes humilis (F.)

The Australian Paper Wasp has been in New Zealand since the turn of the century. Wasps probably found their way here as pupae living inside their nests attached to sheltered areas on early whaling or trading ships from Australia. The Polistes wasps are more aggressive than the Vespulids and they can inflict a nastier sting but, fortunately, this wasp has remained restricted to the warmer parts of the North Island. Unlike their Vespid relatives, the nests of the Polistes are small and not built underground or in houses. They are, however, constructed using the same process of masticating small pieces of weathered wood fibres with saliva. The nests are umbrella-shaped, consisting of just a few cells clustered together and suspended by a slender stalk, often under the eaves of houses.

Adult body length: 15 mm.

Chinese Paper Wasp
Polistes chinensis (F.)

Specimens of the Chinese or Asian Paper Wasp began to appear around Auckland in 1979 and it has rapidly spread as far as Nelson. Unlike the Australian species, nests can be located lower down under window sills or attached to rocks in gardens.

Both paper wasps are reluctant to fly when it is cold; the easiest way to dispose of nests is to gently ease a plastic bag over the nest at night when it is cool, snip the 'stalk', quickly seal the bag and place it immediately in a freezer. Within a few hours the wasps inside the nest will be dead.

Adult body length: 15 mm.

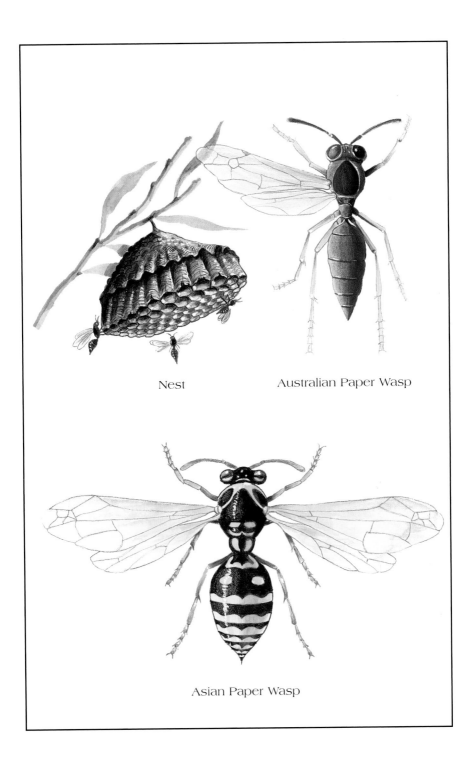

Nest

Australian Paper Wasp

Asian Paper Wasp

Mason Wasp

Pison spinolae Schuckard
Order: HYMENOPTERA
Family: Sphecidae

The Mason Wasp is found in New Zealand, Australia and the
Pacific and belongs to the 'solitary' groups of wasps that build
single-celled nests.

During summer the industrious female chooses nesting sites,
often under bark, but also on walls or even in folds of old coats or
in keyholes. She then gathers up pellets of clay in her jaws and
flies back and forth with them to her building site, where she
moulds the damp clay into a cell. The high-pitched buzzing of the
Mason Wasp building her nest used to be one of the characteristic
sounds of summer in the country but, sadly, it does not seem to
be so frequent today.

After each nest is completed she hunts down and stings an
Orbweb Spider. To humans this sting is usually felt as a harmless
prick but it paralyses the spider. The wasp then carries the spider
to her nest, stuffs it into the cell, lays an egg on it and seals off the
cell. When the larva hatches it rapidly eats the spider, spins a
cocoon to pupate in and finally an adult wasp emerges, chewing
its way out through the hard clay wall.

Adult body length variable from 10–15 mm.

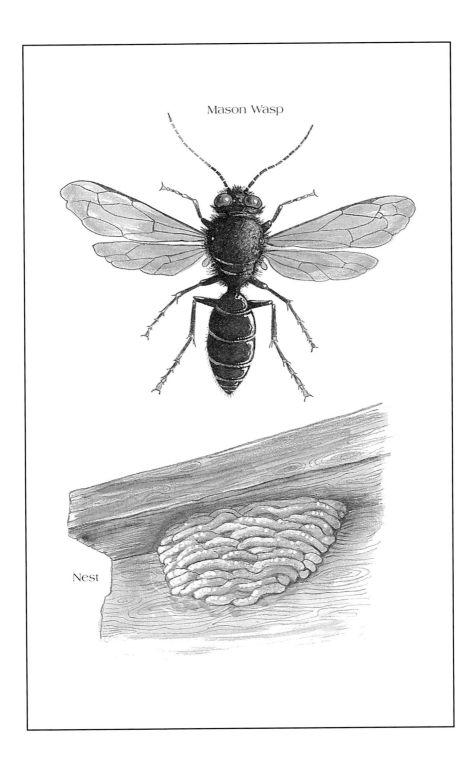

Mason Wasp

Nest

Southern Ant

Monomorium antarcticum (Smith)
Order: HYMENOPTERA
Family: Formicidae

Unlike the rest of the world, New Zealand has very few ant species, with only 40 recorded, of these only ten are native. Although the Southern Ant is probably New Zealand's most common ant it does not come inside houses. It is therefore not as frequently seen as its more domestic relatives, which are attracted to sugary substances and are sometimes a nuisance in houses north of Nelson.

The Southern Ant lives in nests under stones or in rotting logs. In gardens it often nests under warm concrete paths, coming up through the cracks to forage for small insects. It is probably native to New Zealand and is easily recognised by the two humps or nodes at its waist. Its colour is variable, ranging from black to orange.

Many ants follow trails of marker chemicals laid by other ants returning from food — hence the main highways of ants seen on footpaths or in kitchens. In summer, stray, winged ants are often found inside houses. These include the short-lived males and fertilised queens searching for a nesting site to lay their eggs.

Adult body length: 3 mm.

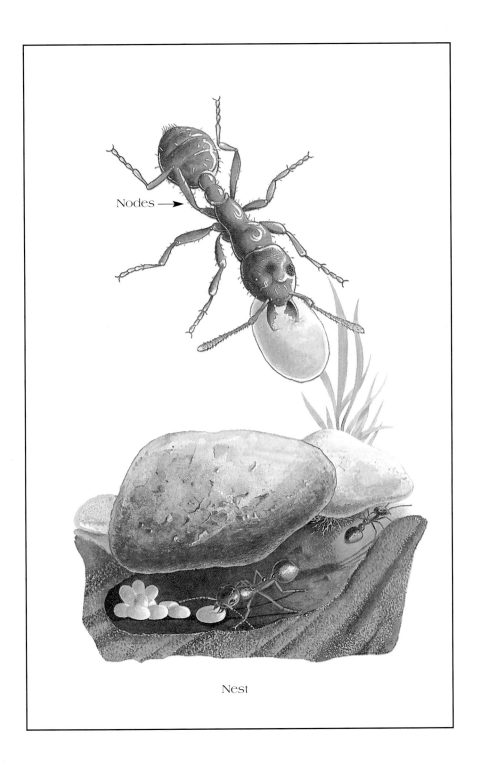

Nodes →

Nest

Insects

in the

bush

Introduction

Most of the estimated 20,000 or more species of insects in New Zealand are found only in native bush habitats. Some very rare species hold a tenuous grip on survival, often restricted to small off-shore islands. Twenty-five are on the endangered species list. The Giant Weta (Wetapunga), for instance, lived in large numbers on the mainland, until predators such as rats and mice were introduced. Even by 1871 they were in decline, as Walter Buller, the famous bird collector, observed. They now survive only on Little Barrier Island.

As native bush habitats have diminished, so have the insects. For instance, the Red Admiral butterfly was reported in abundance by early entomologists. The caterpillars of this native butterfly feed only on stinging nettle, especially the large native species, and it is very probable that as nettles have disappeared so too has the butterfly become scarce. This factor, together with the introduction of the Whitespotted Ichneumonid that feeds on the caterpillars, probably keeps the butterfly numbers at a low level.

New Zealanders are very fond of native plants in their gardens but, with some notable exceptions, many native insects seem unable to follow the plants into modified habitats. For example, there is a native species of thrip that lives only in the folded leaves at the base of flax plants. In spite of intensive searching, this tiny insect has never been found on flax in cultivation.

In the eyes of many New Zealanders dead native trees are only good for firewood but there is more life in a dead tree than in a live one; the grubs living in dead standing trees contribute to sustaining the lives of many of our rare native birds such as Kaka and Kea. Moreover, Kaka will also go to great lengths to dig out Kanuka Longhorn larvae, *Ochrocydus huttoni*, burrowing in live mountain beech as well as having the occasional slurp of honeydew from the Sooty Beech scales living on the bark close by.

To the casual observer the New Zealand bush may appear empty, but in fact insects abound in every conceivable nook and cranny. Searching for insects by torchlight on a summer's night will reveal weevils walking over ferns, beetles crawling on bark, moths feeding from oozing sap and weta eating leaves. During the day many of these insects are hidden away under bark, logs or in old tree holes, while butterflies, wasps and flies are more obvious. No matter where one looks or steps, careful searching will reveal insects boring into twigs, burrowing in bark or rotten wood, or foraging in the leaf litter.

Red Admiral / Kahu kura
Bassaris gonerilla gonerilla (F.)
Order: LEPIDOPTERA
Family: Nymphalidae

The native Red Admiral is called Kahu kura or 'red garment' in Maori and was first discovered by Europeans during Captain Cook's first voyage to New Zealand in 1769. It is found throughout the year but is most common in summer. The Red Admiral is a strong flier, frequently seen in sunny bush glades, but it also visits home gardens. It is often observed resting on tree trunks in the bush, and closer inspection will reveal that the butterfly is intent on feeding from oozing sap.

The butterfly can live for several months. Females lay green eggs on stinging nettle (especially the large native species, *Urtica ferox*), and these hatch after eight or nine days. The caterpillar constructs a tent from a folded leaf and feeds undisturbed inside this protective covering. It develops through five moults over a four- to five-week period. The inconspicuous pupa is frequently attacked by the Whitespotted Ichneumonid wasp (see page 86), a self-introduced parasite. This, as well as its loss of habitat, may be responsible for the decline in Red Admiral numbers, as early entomologists recorded them in abundance.

Adult wingspan variable from 50–60 mm.

Common Copper
Lycaena salustius (F.)
Order: LEPIDOPTERA
Family: Lycaenidae

This butterfly is native to New Zealand. It is especially common in coastal regions but can also be found in most habitats, even up to the alpine zone. It is found throughout the summer and is usually seen fluttering in the vicinity of its common host plant, the tangled creeper pohuehue (*Muehlenbeckia complexa*). The butterflies live for about eight to ten days and overwinter as caterpillars.

Common Coppers breed on the leaves of three species of *Muehlenbeckia* and the eggs take about ten days to hatch. The velvety-green caterpillars usually have a brown stripe down their backs and are rather slug-like in appearance, with their bulging sides tending to conceal the head and legs. They take about 40 days to develop and then pupate among the dry leaves beneath the host plant. About eighteen days later the butterflies emerge.

The Common Copper is the most abundant of four similar, almost indistinguishable, species of copper butterfly. They all breed on *Muehlenbeckia* plants and generally never stray far from them.

Adult wingspan variable from 25–30 mm.

Puriri Moth / Pepe tuna
Aenetus virescens (Doubleday)
Order: LEPIDOPTERA
Family: Hepialidae

The Puriri Moth is New Zealand's largest native moth and is found only in the North Island. It is variable both in wing pattern and colour but is usually green. The Puriri Moth flies at night and early entomologists reported that they flew in swarms. The diminishing of native habitats has probably caused the drop in numbers but they also fall prey to owls and cats. The moth is attracted to lights and their fluttering appearance has given them the alternative name of Ghost Moth.

The caterpillars probably live for at least three years and spend the early part of their life on the forest floor living on fungus. Older ones bore '7'-shaped tunnels, usually in puriri trees, and feed on live callus tissue at the entrance hole that is protected by a camouflaged cover of webbing. Weta often shelter in old holes once the Puriri Moth caterpillar has emerged.

Although the moths can be found throughout the year, they are most common between September and November. They do not feed and females may lay up to 2000 eggs, which are scattered haphazardly over the forest floor.

Adult wingspan variable from 75–150 mm.

Female

Male

Five-finger Plume Moth
Aciptilia monospilalis Walker
Order: LEPIDOPTERA
Family: Pterophoridae

Plume moths can be distinguished from all other moths by their characteristic T-shape when resting and by their very long legs and feather-like wings. There are about 22 species of plume moths in New Zealand, all but one of which are native. The Five-finger Plume Moth is one of the most commonly seen species and it has two colour forms — brown, as in the illustration, and also pure white. Its slug-like caterpillars are green and hairy. As its common name suggests, the moth scrapes oblong windows in five-finger (*Pseudopanax arboreus*) and also ivy leaves.

Adult wingspan: 20 mm.

Common Forest Looper
Pseudocoremia suavis Butler
Order: LEPIDOPTERA
Family: Geometridae

The Common Forest Looper usually catches the eye with a yellow flash of its hind wings as it flits among trees in the bush. However, when the insect rests on a tree trunk these colourful hind wings are tucked away under the forewings, which have a bark-like pattern that blends in with the surroundings.

There are many species of forest looper moths in New Zealand, but the one illustrated is the most frequently encountered. The Common Forest Looper caterpillar feeds on beech (*Nothofagus* species), kamahi and rata leaves. When disturbed, it freezes in a twig-like pose.

Adult wingspan: 30 mm.

fivefinger plume moth

common forest looper

Antlion

Weeleus acutus (Walker)
Order: NEUROPTERA
Family: Myrmeleontidae

The sensation of trying to climb up the walls of a crumbling sand dune must be similar to that of an Antlion's victim struggling to escape from the funnel-shaped pit trap into which it has fallen. Eventually the exhausted victim (usually a small insect) slides to the bottom, where it is seized in the caliper-shaped jaws of the concealed Antlion. A fluid is then injected to dissolve the body tissues before they are sucked dry.

Antlion pit traps are found in sunny, undisturbed positions in the shelter of overhanging banks, rocks or even old verandahs — wherever there is dry, friable soil. A newly hatched larva constructs a pit by first scooping the soil away with its abdomen in an anticlockwise motion. As the pit deepens the larva discards the unwanted soil by tossing it out with a flick of its flattened head.

The native Antlion is the larva of an elegant 'lacewing' adult, which is a sluggish flier. Although sometimes attracted to lights, it is not frequently seen.

Adult wingspan variable from 60–70 mm.

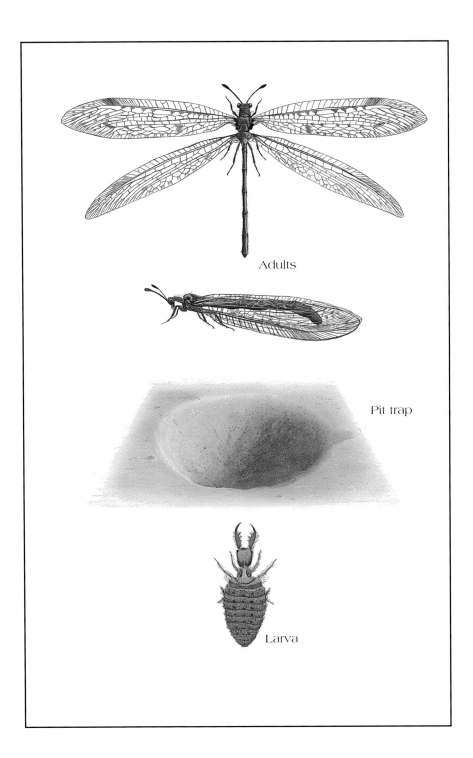

Adults

Pit trap

Larva

Carabid Beetle

Megadromus capito (White)
Order: COLEOPTERA
Family: Carabidae

Most of the many different species of carabids or ground beetles in New Zealand are unique to this country (see page 46). Many have no wings and live only in restricted areas of native bush. However, the wingless species illustrated is comparatively widespread in the North Island, being found from East Cape to Wellington. A closely related and very similar species, *Megadromus antarcticus*, is common on the Canterbury Plains in the South Island.

Like all Carabid Beetles, both these species are predatory, living under logs in the bush during the day and emerging at night to search for small invertebrates, which are snatched up in their powerful, pincer-like jaws. These beetles can give a painful nip if picked up the wrong way, and some species may also produce a foul-smelling defensive liquid.

The larvae are also predatory, living in the ground or under logs. Unlike other Carabid Beetles, the adult female shown here remains with her eggs and young larvae when they hatch.

Adult body length variable from 20–25 mm.

Common Tiger Beetle
Neocicindela tuberculata (F.)
Order: COLEOPTERA
Family: Carabidae

The Common Tiger Beetle shown here is one of twelve species of native tiger beetles found in New Zealand. It is common in the North Island and in Nelson and the Marlborough Sounds. On hot summer days tiger beetles can be seen running back and forth on open, sunny ground, especially clay banks and sandy areas, searching for insects which they run down and seize in their sharp, sickle-shaped jaws.

The larva lives in a burrow and its modified head, with both eyes directed to the surface, enables it to watch and seize prey, which it then drags down into its burrow to eat. In winter the larva plugs the burrow entrance and hibernates until spring. The life cycle may take several years, but each spring some larvae pupate and emerge as adults.

In the past children nicknamed the larva 'Butcher Boy' or 'Penny Doctor' and made a game of fishing out the larva with a piece of straw poked down the burrow. Unfortunately, the disappearance of natural habitats close to where most children play has made these names obsolete.

Adult body length: 10 mm.

Reticulate Stag Beetle
Lissotes reticulatus (Westwood)
Order: COLEOPTERA
Family: Lucanidae

There are around 30 species of stag beetles in New Zealand.
Some flightless species are very rare, surviving only on offshore
islands or in some restricted areas of bush on the mainland.
Moreover, as habitats have diminished, so too have overall beetle
numbers, and several species in New Zealand are threatened with
extinction.

The native Reticulate Stag Beetle, however, is still widespread
and common. It is a strong flier and is sometimes attracted to
lights. If handled roughly the beetle can give a painful nip with its
powerful jaws. Its common name refers to the net-like pattern on
its back. 'Stag' Beetle is the name given to all the beetles of the
family Lucanidae because the males of some foreign species have
remarkable antler-like jaws.

The larvae look rather like those of Grass Grubs (see page 50),
but the end of the abdomen is a little more bulbous. Beetles
and larvae live and feed on decaying wood and are often found
together under dead logs.

Adult body length: 17 mm.

Male

Female

Manuka Beetle / Kekerewai

Pyronota festiva (F.)
Order: COLEOPTERA
Family: Scarabaeidae

The Manuka Beetle was first collected during Captain Cook's voyage in 1769, probably at Ship Cove in the Marlborough Sounds. One of these very old specimens still exists in Joseph Banks' collection of insects at the British Museum, London.

This small native beetle is common all over New Zealand during summer. It feeds especially on manuka (*Leptospermum scoparium*), and on warm days large numbers gather in the flowers. Many fall into streams where they are snapped up by hungry trout. Some 180 beetles have been recorded from one trout stomach alone. Maori named the beetle Kekerewai, meaning 'to float on water', and ate them crushed and baked with bulrush pollen as a kind of scone.

The larvae look much like the closely related Grass Grub (see page 50) and live in the ground, feeding on roots during the winter and emerging as adults in the spring. As the illustration indicates, there are several colour forms of this Manuka Beetle, but many other closely related and similar-looking beetles are also found in New Zealand (see page 118).

Adult body length: 8 mm.

Chafer Beetles
Order: COLEOPTERA
Family: Scarabaeidae

Mumu Chafer
Stethaspis longicornis Arrow

Tanguru Chafer
Stethaspis suturalis (F.)

Stethaspis belongs to a subfamily of the Scarab beetles called
Chafers or Cockchafers, of which there are about 70 species found
in New Zealand.

The beetles emerge *en masse* from the ground on warm, still
evenings in early summer, attracting attention with their erratic
flight and buzzing noise. They are common in bush habitats
although they also occur in exotic plantations. The larvae resemble
their close relatives, the common Grass Grubs (see page 50), but
are much larger and feed on tree roots.

The Mumu Chafer is found in the North Island as far south as
the Volcanic Plateau and Taranaki. Further south it is replaced by
the Tanguru Chafer, which extends down to Nelson. The two
species can be easily distinguished; only the Tanguru Chafer
has the yellow stripe down the centre of its back.

Adult body lengths: 20 mm.

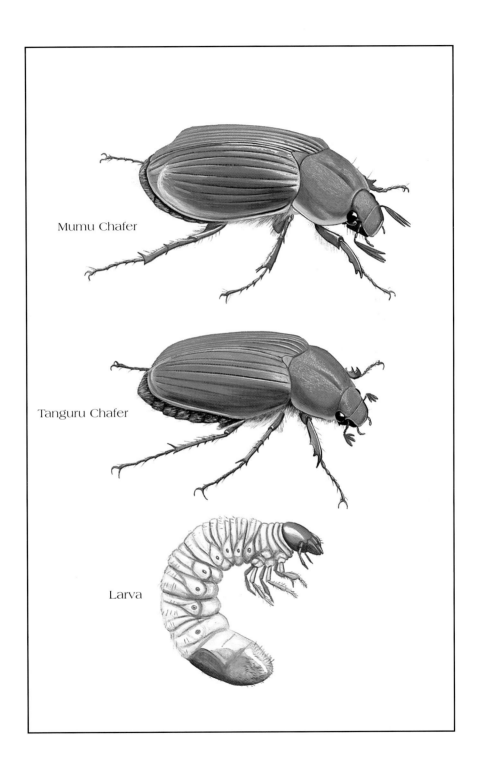

Mumu Chafer

Tanguru Chafer

Larva

Flower Longhorn Beetles
Zorion species
Order: COLEOPTERA
Family: Cerambycidae

These minute Longhorn Beetles are probably the most strikingly coloured beetles we have in New Zealand, but their size is such that they are frequently overlooked. They are very common and can often be found feeding in native flowers.

There are about six named species of native *Zorion* beetles in New Zealand but there is a great deal of confusion over their classification. There appear to be several colour forms, the commonest being blue with yellow spots or alternatively orange with yellow spots in blue circles. However, in some localities these colour forms merge into bewildering variations on the theme, and experts have not yet been able to decide just how many species exist.

Flower Longhorn Beetles breed in dead branches or under the bark of many different trees, but little is known of their biology.

Adult body length: 5 mm.

Huhu Beetle
Prionoplus reticularis White
Order: COLEOPTERA
Family: Cerambycidae

The native Huhu is New Zealand's largest and heaviest beetle and its grubs were a particular Maori delicacy. The noisy, erratic flight of the adult beetle may cause alarm when it blunders into lights, and if handled roughly the beetle can give a painful nip — which may explain its other common name of Haircutter. The name *reticularis* refers to the net-like pattern on its back.

The beetle lives in both native and exotic trees and takes up to three years to complete its life cycle. Clusters of eggs are laid under bark or in crevices and hatch after three to four weeks. The larvae eat and tunnel their way through rotten wood, leaving behind loosely packed chewings rather like curled wood shavings and faecal material or frass. Eventually the larvae may almost completely eat away a log, leaving only its thin outer shell. In spring the mature grub builds a chamber lined with shredded wood and frass in which to pupate. A few weeks later the adult beetle emerges, using its powerful mandibles to bore its way out to the surface. The beetle does not feed and lives only for about two weeks.

Adult body length variable from 25–50 mm.

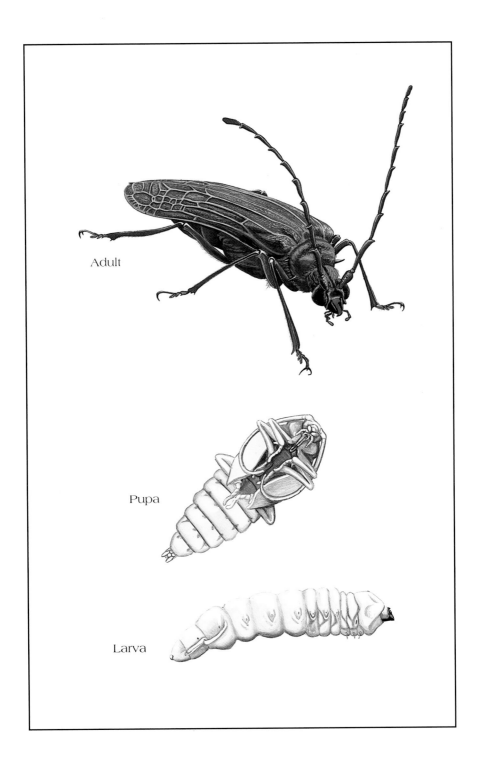

Adult

Pupa

Larva

Elephant Weevil
Rhyncodes ursus White
Order: COLEOPTERA
Family: Curculionidae

Because of the bulky shape of this native weevil it has been given the scientific name *ursus*, meaning 'bear-like'. Elephant Weevils are usually found where beech (*Nothofagus* species) grows and are more likely to be seen at night as they wander ponderously over beech trunks. The colour pattern is formed by tiny hairs and gives the weevil a good camouflage on a background of beech bark, but in older weevils these hairs are often rubbed off, giving them a dull black appearance.

Elephant Weevil larvae are maggot-like with no legs, but they have a well-developed head and strong chewing jaws for boring into solid trunks and branches of dead beech. Adults vary in size depending on how much wood the larvae have eaten. The larvae are parasitised by the native Giant Ichneumonid wasp, which is sometimes seen flying around beech trees in search of them.

Adult body length variable from 10–20 mm.

Giraffe Weevil / Tuwhaipapa

Lasiorhynchus barbicornis (F.)
Order: COLEOPTERA
Family: Brentidae

The Maori name for this spectacular weevil, Tuwhaipapa, refers to the god of a newly made canoe. It belongs to a family of weevils distinguished by their straight antennae. (Other close relatives have elbow-shaped antennae; see page 125).

The strong, wood-chewing jaws at the end of the long, slender snout are interesting, for they are operated by exceptionally long muscles anchored far back in the head. On the male the antennae are situated at the very tip of the snout, but on the smaller female they are further back towards the head. This leaves part of the female's snout free for chewing holes in the trees where eggs are laid. When the eggs hatch, the larvae bore into the trees where they feed and develop until they emerge as adult weevils in the spring.

Adult Giraffe Weevils are found in summer on trunks and logs in native bush, sometimes congregating in large numbers. Up to 60 have been found on one tree alone.

Adult body length variable from 15–80 mm.

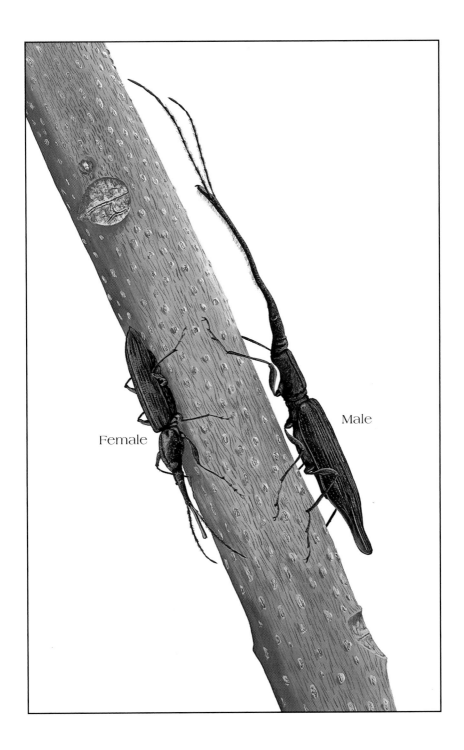

Female

Male

127

New Zealand Glow-worm

Arachnocampa luminosa (Skuse)
Order: DIPTERA
Family: Keroplatidae

The New Zealand Glow-worm lives in damp caves, tunnels, over-hanging banks and old tree roots. When the insect is disturbed, the characteristic glow that comes from the end of the abdomen can be quickly doused by the insect withdrawing the 'light organ' into its body.

The worm-like larva suspends itself in a web hammock anchored at each end by stout threads, and from this it dangles many 'fishing lines' covered with sticky droplets. The glowing larva waits patiently in its hammock until a small insect is attracted to its light and becomes entangled in one of its lines like a spider. Sensing the vibrations, the glow-worm larva hauls up the struggling victim and eats it. Faecal material and food remains are carefully lowered on threads until they drop off.

The adult fly also glows, but it lives for only a brief two to three days. The female lays about 80 eggs that take two to three weeks to hatch, but the larvae take about nine months to develop.

Adult body length: 10 mm.

Larva

Adult

Common Northern Robber Fly

Neoitamus melanopogon Schiner
Order: DIPTERA
Family: Asilidae

When you are walking through the bush a Robber Fly may alight briefly on your arm or shoulder, but it will not harm you. This perch makes a good observation post for the Robber Fly, which darts upon prospective victims and seizes them on the wing. Robber Flies often catch insects almost as large as themselves, trapping them between their long, sturdy legs that are fitted out with large claws. The Robber Fly pierces the victim with its ridged proboscis and injects a fluid that quietens the insect and dissolves the body tissue which is then sucked out.

There are about 25 species of Robber Flies in New Zealand. The one illustrated is commonly found hunting in sunny bush clearings.

Adult body length: 15 mm.

Large Hover Fly

Melangyna novaezealandiae (Macquart)
Order: DIPTERA
Family: Syrphidae

There are about ten species of small hover flies similar to the one illustrated. They are often seen on sunny days hovering rather like hummingbirds, with their wings beating so fast that they appear just a blur. They dart about near flowers, resting only briefly to feed on nectar. The larvae are usually predatory, attacking and feeding on aphids and small caterpillars.

Adult body length: 10 mm.

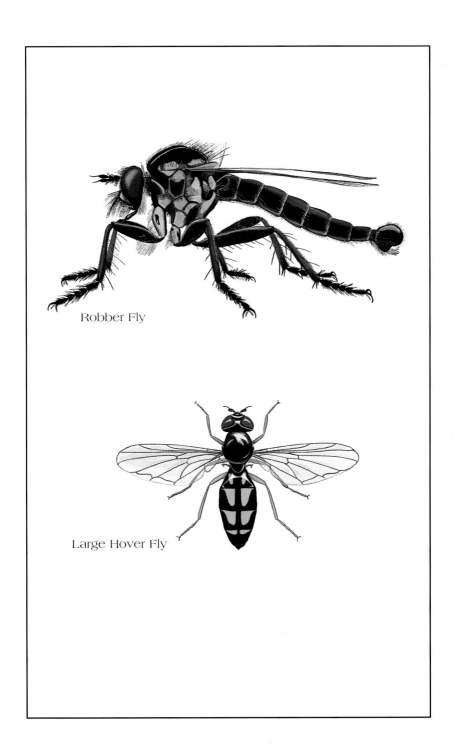

Robber Fly

Large Hover Fly

New Zealand Blue Blow Fly
Calliphora quadrimaculata (Svederus)
Order: DIPTERA
Family: Calliphoridae

The native Blue Blow Fly is very difficult to distinguish from its close relative, the European Blow Fly (see page 66), but it is more common in bush habitats. Adult Blue Blow Flies are often seen visiting native flowers but very little is known about their biology. The larvae are thought to feed in the bush on decaying animal matter — dead birds and animals probably being an important food source. Early settlers were very aware of the Blue Blow Fly's annoying habit of laying eggs on, or 'blowing', woollen fabric.

Adult body length: 10 mm.

Giant Hairy Tachinid
Protohystricia species
Order: DIPTERA
Family: Tachinidae

Over 150 species of tachinids are found in New Zealand, most of them in alpine habitats, and the Giant Hairy Tachinid is just one of them. It is a parasite of native Porina caterpillars and on warm, sunny days can be seen flying over undisturbed grassland in search of them. The species illustrated is one of three similar native species that occur south of Auckland.

Adult body length variable from 10–15 mm.

New Zealand
Blue Blow Fly

Giant Hairy Tachinid

Wellington Tree Weta

Hemideina crassidens (Blanchard)
Order: ORTHOPTERA
Family: Anostomatidae

The Wellington Tree Weta is the most common weta in New Zealand and is found from Mount Taranaki and Ruapehu in the North Island south to Nelson and the West Coast of the South Island. The male has an enormous head and massive jaws and the female, illustrated here, has a long, curved ovipositor that, despite its appearance, is not a sting but is used for egg laying.

Weta (sometimes called Taepo) hide under bark or in old insect holes during the day and come out at night to browse on vegetation. They can live for up to two years and are found both in bush habitats and in gardens. Despite their rather fearsome appearance, they are shy, inoffensive creatures that can inflict a painful bite only if handled roughly. When disturbed they may strike a spectacular, aggressive pose, raising their spiny hind legs up over the body then rapidly jerking them down, thereby producing an angry rasping sound.

There are at least 26 native species of weta in New Zealand, as well as the closely related family of Cave Weta (see page 136). They live in the bush as well as under rocks in the alpine zone. In spite of their large size, new species are still being discovered, the most recent being a Tusked Weta on the east coast of the North Island.

Adult body length variable from 50–65 mm.

Cave Weta
Gymnoplectron edwardsii (Scudder)
Order: ORTHOPTERA
Family: Rhaphidophoridae

The 50 or so species of native Cave Weta in New Zealand can be distinguished from the other family of weta (see page 134) by their exceptionally long antennae, relatively small body and long and delicate but prickly legs. The very long hind legs with muscular-looking 'thighs' or femora are specially adapted for jumping.

Cave Weta normally live in dark, damp, cool places such as caves and tunnels, where they congregate in large numbers, or they live under bark and fallen logs, where they are usually found individually. There are, however, unusual species living high up in the Southern Alps that tend to congregate around rocky outcrops. Cave Weta are known to eat decaying vegetable matter and live plant material, or they are cannibalistic.

The species illustrated here lives in caves or under logs and bark in the bush, coming out at night to browse on the forest floor.

Adult body length variable from 15–25 mm.

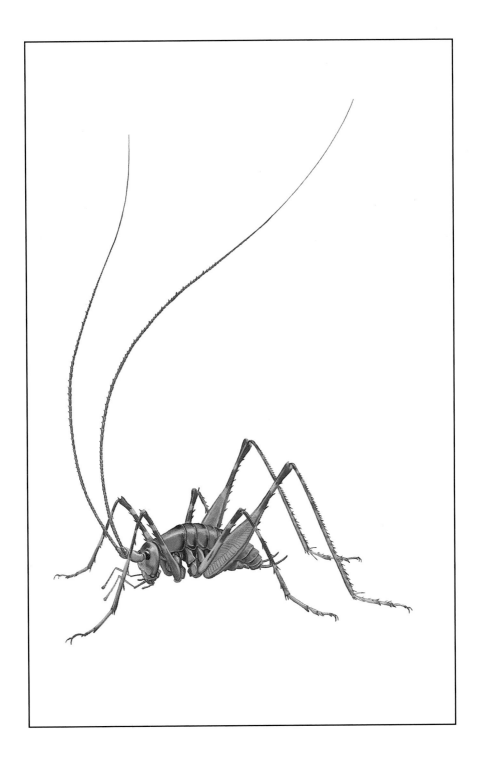

Black Cockroach / Kekerengu

Platyzosteria novaeseelandiae (Brunner)
Order: BLATTODEA
Family: Blattidae

The Black Cockroach has one of the most unpleasant smells of any native New Zealand insect. If handled or disturbed it emits a foul-smelling fluid through special glands near the end of the abdomen. The chemical compounds involved have been analysed and have been found to include some that are also in the defensive secretion of the Green Vegetable Bug (see page 44).

Black Cockroaches are usually found in bush habitats but are sometimes brought into houses with firewood. They are wingless and their flattened shape enables them to squeeze into dark crevices under bark or in wood heaps. There they hide during the day, coming out only at night to scavenge on the forest floor. If uncovered during the day they quickly scuttle for cover. The female lays a purse-shaped egg case from which many small cockroaches emerge, developing through a series of moults until they become adults.

Adult body length: 20 mm.

Prickly Stick Insect / Ro / Whe

Acanthoxyla prasina (Westwood)
Order: PHASMATODEA
Family: Phasmatidae

There are about 30 species of stick insects, or 'walking sticks', native to New Zealand. The Prickly Stick Insect usually feeds on manuka (*Leptospermum scoparium*) leaves. If disturbed, it freezes with its front legs pointing forward so that it looks even more like a stick, sometimes gently swaying. Ancient Maori lore suggested that the sex of an unborn child could be determined by whether a Stick Insect or Praying Mantis alighted on a pregnant woman.

The Prickly Stick Insect has no males and reproduces partheno-genetically; that is, without fertilisation. Seed-like egg capsules are dropped haphazardly on the ground where they lie dormant until spring. A miniature stick insect then emerges and after several moults it reaches maturity. Some Prickly Stick Insects are brown and others green. They can alter their shade to some extent, depending on the plant they are resting on, but they cannot change completely from one colour to the other.

Adult body length variable from 70–90 mm.

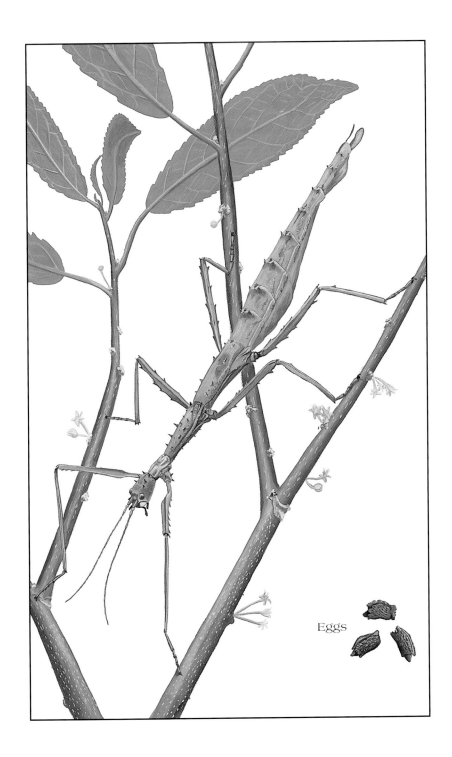

Eggs

141

Golden Hunting Wasp

Sphictostethus nitidus (F.)
Order: HYMENOPTERA
Family: Pompilidae

Spider Wasps are often seen on sunny clay banks, swiftly darting about in search of live spiders. Often there is a relentless pursuit until the victim is pounced upon. Then the wasp stings the spider, leaving it paralysed but still alive. She then flies away, carrying the stunned victim bunched up in her long legs, or, if the spider is too heavy, drags it along the ground to its already evacuated nest. The wasp stuffs the spider into the nest, lays an egg on it and plugs the entrance hole. When the wasp egg hatches, the larva eats the still-fresh contents of the spider, pupates and then emerges as an adult wasp, digging its way out of the nest.

In New Zealand there are at least eleven species of Spider Wasps, of which ten are found nowhere else in the world. The species illustrated is the largest of the native Golden Spider Wasps that can be found in most open habitats, including home gardens.

There is an even larger black species, *Priocnemis (Trichocurgus) monachus*, which has iridescent wings and hunts Funnel-web and Trap-door spiders whose burrows lack lids. It will also chase other spiders from their webs and often a battle will ensue, the spider rearing its front legs. The agile wasp will quickly sting the exposed abdomen to paralyse its victim before dragging it off to its nest.

Adult body length variable from 10–15 mm.

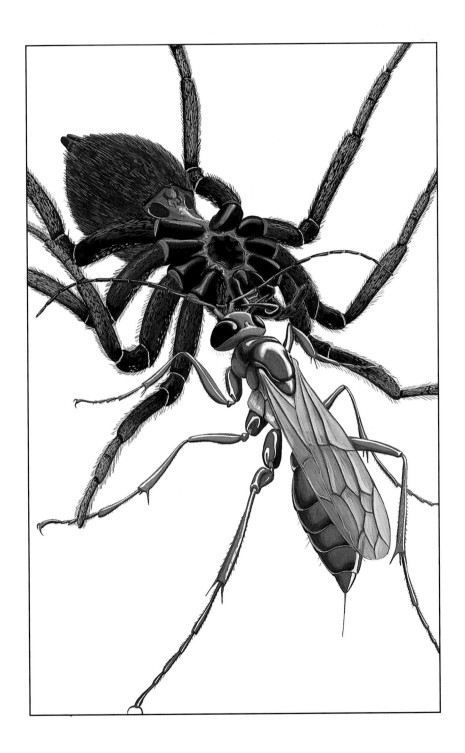

143

Insects
in
fresh water

Introduction

In this section most types of aquatic insects are represented. The various species mentioned can usually be found in lakes, streams, rivers, bogs or even brackish water but rarely are insects found living in salt water.

Aquatic insects are especially vulnerable to poor quality water. For example, Mayfly nymphs are very common and widespread in rivers, lakes and streams and their absence can be an important indicator of water pollution. Some, like the Backswimmer, spend all their life under water while others, such as Caddisflies, have a long aquatic larval stage and then a brief flying adult stage.

Aquatic larval stages are best observed by carefully disturbing rocks and debris under water then filtering the water by holding a small, submerged nylon net in the backwash. In more stagnant water the net can be dredged through pond weed or muddy bottom ooze. The trapped insects can then be tipped out and observed in a white, shallow tray filled with the same water (not foreign tap water). Return the specimens to their original habitat as soon as possible or they will die.

Adults of aquatic insects never stray far from where they have emerged, and sweeping or beating along streamside vegetation during the day will dislodge adults resting before their brief night-time activity.

Damselflies
Order: ODONATA
Suborder: Zygoptera

Blue Damselfly / Kekewai
Austrolestes colensonis (White)

Australian Damselfly
Ischnura aurora aurora (Brauer)

Red Damselfly / Kihitara
Xanthocnemis zealandica (McLachlan)

On sunny days damselflies are seen either flitting about over lakes, streams and bogs searching for small insects, or resting with their wings held together vertically over their bodies. Mating pairs are often seen flying in tandem, with the male in front grasping the female behind the head with claspers at the end of its abdomen.

There are only three species of damselfly in New Zealand and their colours differ between sexes. The male of the native Blue Damselfly is brilliant blue and black while the female is greener. The tiny male Australian Damselfly, on the other hand, has a red abdomen and a blue tip, and the female is mainly a dull greeny-yellow. This species is restricted to the North Island. The common Red Damselfly has red males but the females are usually bronzy-black except for some that can be red.

Damselfly nymphs are aquatic, with external breathing gills in the form of three leaf-like projections at the end of the abdomen. They are predatory and hunt under water among stones and plants.

Adult body length of Blue Damselfly: 42 mm; Australian Damselfly: 25 mm and Red Damselfly: 32 mm.

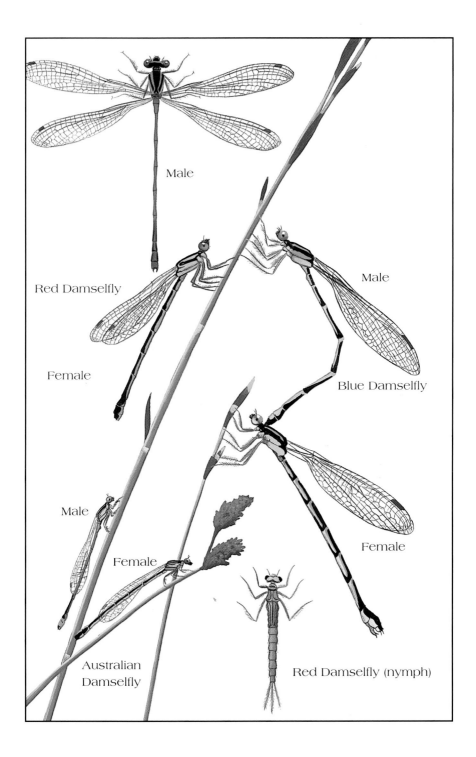

Male

Red Damselfly

Female

Male

Blue Damselfly

Female

Male

Female

Australian
Damselfly

Red Damselfly (nymph)

Giant Dragonfly / Kapokapowai

Uropetala carovei (White)
Order: ODONATA
Suborder: Anisoptera

Dragonflies are fierce predators in the insect world but are completely harmless to people. Their swift, darting flight is not just idle play but an industrious search for prey. With their swivelling head and enormous eyes, they hunt down flying insects that are seized with their grasping legs.

Dragonflies can be distinguished from their smaller damselfly relatives (see page 148) in that they normally rest with their wings lying flat, not vertical. The native Giant Dragonfly is the largest of the ten species found in New Zealand.

In contrast to the splendid adult, Giant Dragonfly nymphs are rather ugly creatures, usually encrusted with mud. They live in tunnels in permanently moist seepage areas during the four years or more they take to develop. At night they lurk at the entrance holes of their tunnels and wait for unsuspecting insects to pass by. The lower part of the mouth is modified into a hinged, elbow-shaped structure or 'mask', which can be shot out to grab the victim.

Adult wingspan variable from 100–115 mm.

Adult

Nymph

Mayflies
Order: EPHEMEROPTERA

There are at least 33 similar species of Mayflies in New Zealand. Adults can be recognised by their three variable tail filaments and delicate wings, which are held together vertically when the mayfly is resting.

Mayfly nymphs are aquatic, with external gills and three tail filaments of varying lengths. Their flattened shape and sturdy legs enable them to live in flowing water, where they are commonly found feeding on minute plant life under stones. Because the nymphs are so common and widespread, their absence can be an important indicator of water pollution.

Mature Mayfly nymphs emerge from the water and moult into what anglers call 'duns' with dull-coloured wings. These do not feed and sometimes last for less than a day before moulting again into short-lived adults called 'spinners', which fly over water at dusk in an undulating mating dance. As the females dip into the water to lay eggs they risk being snatched up by trout.

Adult body length variable from 5–20 mm.

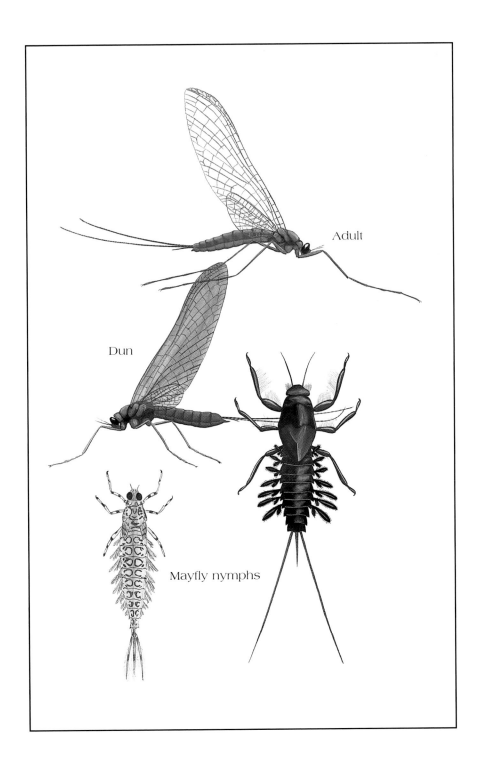

Adult

Dun

Mayfly nymphs

Caddisflies
Order: TRICHOPTERA

These moth-like insects can be distinguished from true moths by their long antennae and distinct hairy wings which fold tent-like over their bodies. Caddisflies are attracted to lights and are usually encountered as bothersome intruders in houses close to streams and lakes. At dusk and on into the evening they can be seen flying in swarms over calm water. These swarms are frequently encountered by anglers during the evening rise.

New Zealand has nearly 150 species of Caddisflies. While varying in size, they are otherwise very similar in appearance. The larvae, however, can be roughly divided into three groups. The most common type construct portable tube- or snail-shaped cases of tiny stones or debris; other types spin a net, and others are free living.

Caddisflies are called 'sedges' by anglers and they are a particular delicacy of trout. Over 864 caddisfly larvae have been recorded in one trout stomach alone in New Zealand. Caddisfly larvae may be mistaken for caterpillars, having a long segmented body, a head capsule with small eyes and six legs. They are either predatory or herbivorous and spend their entire immature stage in water.

Adult length with wings folded variable from 10–15 mm.

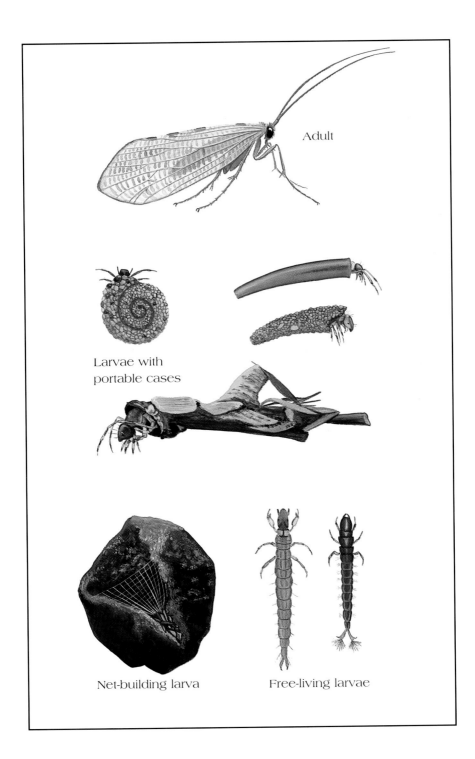

Adult

Larvae with
portable cases

Net-building larva   Free-living larvae

Dobsonfly
Archichauliodes diversus (Walker)
Order: MEGALOPTERA
Family: Corydalidae

The Dobsonfly is one of our largest aquatic insects and is native to New Zealand. The larvae are commonly called 'creepers' or 'toe biters' as they have powerful jaws for catching their prey, normally Mayfly nymphs. They live in running water, hiding during the day under stones and coming out at night to feed. Although they look like centipedes with many legs, most of these 'legs' are really gills; there are only three pairs of true legs behind the head.

Mature larvae leave the water and burrow under stones beside streams to rest for about four months before pupating. This pre-pupal stage is favourite trout bait, but searching anglers who fail to replace stones and thus destroy their pupation sites can deplete Dobsonfly populations.

Adults have huge wings but are clumsy fliers and often blunder into lights. They are found from December to March but do not feed and live only for about six to ten days. Egg masses are laid on exposed boulders or vegetation. After about two weeks the eggs hatch and the tiny larvae drop into the water.

Adult length with wings folded variable from 25–35 mm.

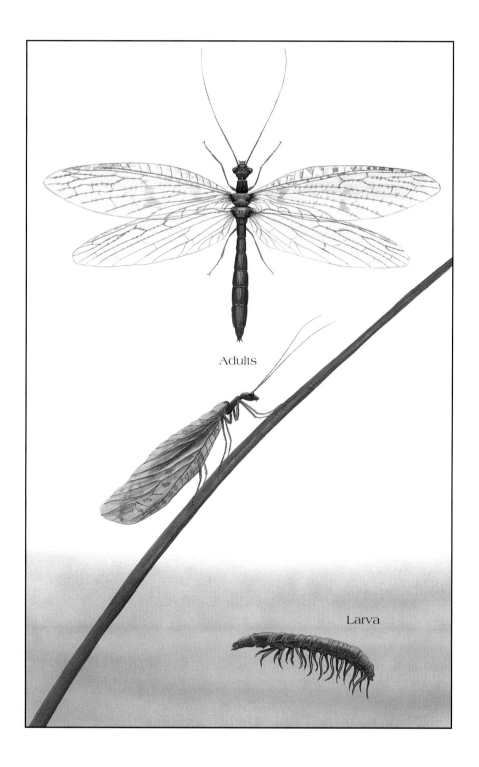

Adults

Larva

157

Large Green Stonefly

Stenoperla prasina (Newman)
Order: PLECOPTERA
Family: Eustheniidae

This native stonefly is one of two similar species, but the Large Green Stonefly is more common and is found from sea level to the alpine zone. During the day it usually hides in vegetation along stream banks, resting with its large, soft, filmy wings folded over its body. Although a weak flier, it is attracted to lights and its blundering flight around lamps is familiar to those who live close to streams and rivers.

Large Green Stonefly nymphs live in clear, stony streams with a reasonably strong current. They are carnivorous, feeding mainly on small Mayfly nymphs. Stonefly nymphs have gills but can be distinguished from the similar Mayfly nymphs (see page 152) by having only two filaments instead of three, longer antennae and characteristic elbow-shaped legs.

There are about 55 other species of Stoneflies found in New Zealand, but these are usually brown. Some wingless species live high up in the Southern Alps where the larvae are not aquatic but live in humid cavities under plants and stones.

Adult length with wings folded variable from 20–30 mm.

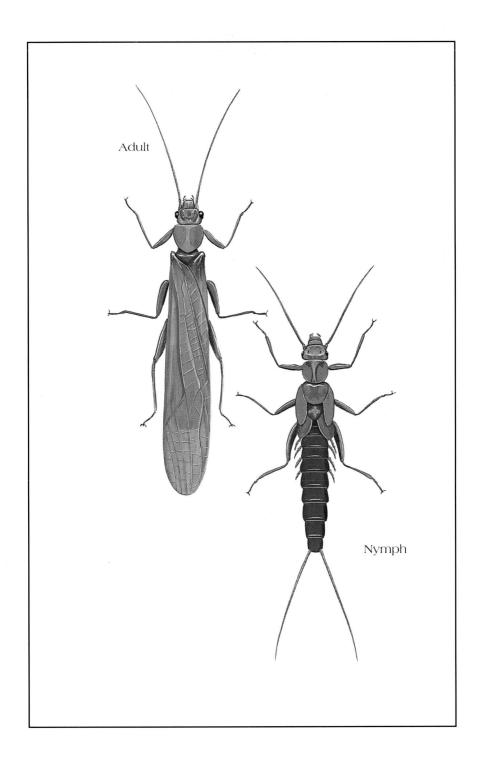

Adult

Nymph

Common Water Boatman

Sigara arguta (White)
Order: HEMIPTERA
Family: Corixidae

The native Common Water Boatman lives and breeds in freshwater ponds. It replenishes its air supply by quick visits to the surface and feeds by filtering muddy bottom ooze that it scoops up with its shovel-shaped front legs. The Water Boatman's powerful hind legs propel it through the water and the middle pair act as anchors while it feeds.

Adult body length: 5 mm.

Common Backswimmer

Anisops assimilis White
Order: HEMIPTERA
Family: Notonectidae

The native Common Backswimmer has a keel-shaped back. It lies upside down in the water and propels itself along in swift, jerky movements with long, oar-like hind legs. At rest, these are held in a V shape, pointing towards the tail while the remaining legs are tucked away close to the body and conceal a stout, sucking 'beak'. The Backswimmer has huge eyes that reach right around the head and enable it to see upside down and to attack small aquatic insects. Some Backswimmers have either fully or partly developed wings.

Like the Common Water Boatman, it lives and breeds in ponds and must also replenish its air supply by quick visits to the surface.

Adult body length: 7 mm.

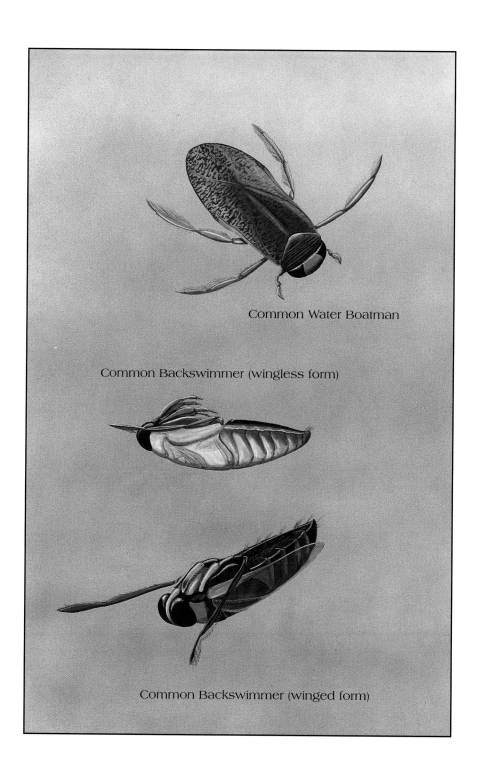

Common Water Boatman

Common Backswimmer (wingless form)

Common Backswimmer (winged form)

Cosmopolitan Diving Beetle

Rhantus pulverosus (Stephens)
Order: COLEOPTERA
Family: Dytiscidae

This predatory water beetle is sometimes attracted to lights but normally lives in ponds and stream backwaters. It is fascinating to observe how the Cosmopolitan Diving Beetle has adapted to living under water. Keep one in a fish tank and feed it with tiny pieces of fresh meat. Watch how it replenishes the air supply under its elytra by hanging momentarily upside down, with only the tip of its abdomen above the water surface, before diving down again, often carrying an extra air bubble behind it.

The long, densely fringed hind legs of the Cosmopolitan Diving Beetle are used like oars, giving a jerky swimming motion. Surprisingly, the beetle is also a strong flier and is widely distributed throughout the world.

The larvae are also predatory and live in similar habitats to the adults. Unlike many other aquatic insects that have external breathing gills, water beetle larvae breathe in a similar fashion to the adults, obtaining their air supply from the surface.

Adult body length: 11 mm.

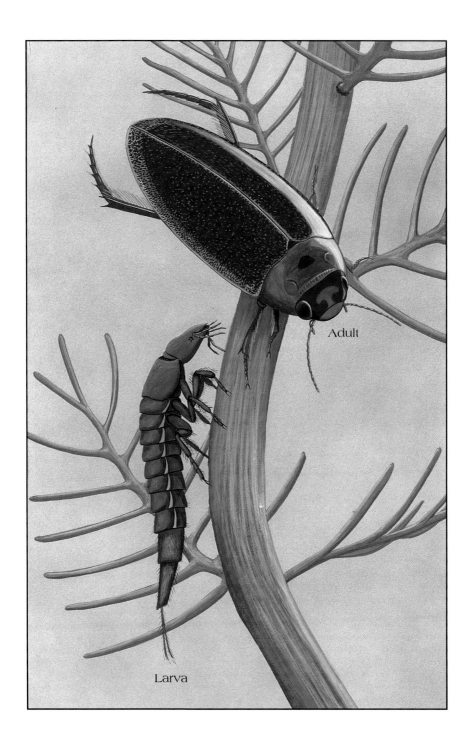

Adult

Larva

Sand Fly / Namu
Austrosimulium australense (Schiner)
Order: DIPTERA
Family: Simuliidae

In New Zealand these insects are traditionally called Sand Flies, but in other countries they are called Black Flies. Some foreign species transmit human diseases, but all species in New Zealand, although annoying, are quite harmless. It is only the female Sand Fly that sucks blood and she is most active at dawn and dusk. Only two of the eleven native species found in New Zealand bite humans; another attacks penguins and the remainder probably bite other birds.

Sand Flies breed in flowing water, usually in small streams and ditches. The female, enclosed in an air bubble, crawls under the water and lays her eggs under submerged plants or stones. Larvae are often found grouped together under rocks and feed by filtering water. Sand Fly pupae anchor themselves in sheltered places to pupate and have characteristic branched respiratory organs. The biting species of Sand Fly illustrated breeds in streams where the larvae attach themselves to vegetation dangling in the water.

Adult body length: 2 mm.

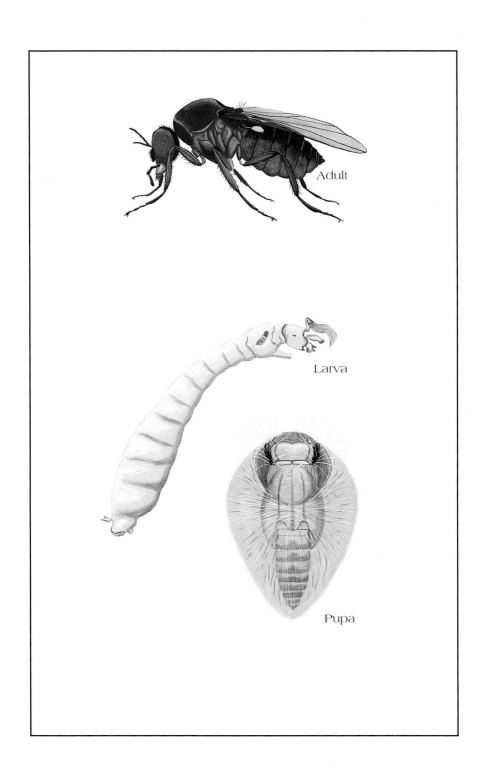

Adult

Larva

Pupa

Vigilant Mosquito / Waeroa

Culex pervigilans Bergroth
Order: DIPTERA
Family: Culicidae

Although mosquitoes in other parts of the world are vectors or carriers of human diseases, the fifteen species found in New Zealand (twelve are native) are, luckily, harmless to us. Male mosquitoes have characteristic plume-like antennae but are difficult to detect, for only the female bites.

Mosquitoes breed in stagnant water and both larvae and pupae swim freely with a characteristic wriggle. Larvae feed by filtering microscopic organisms and detritus from the water and breathe through a siphon that protrudes through the water surface while the larva hangs upside down. The pupa, on the other hand, hangs upright from the water surface to breathe through tubes on the back of the head.

The native Vigilant Mosquito is nocturnal and breeds in both fresh and brackish water. Females lay eggs in raft-like clusters which float on the surface.

Adult body length: 5 mm.

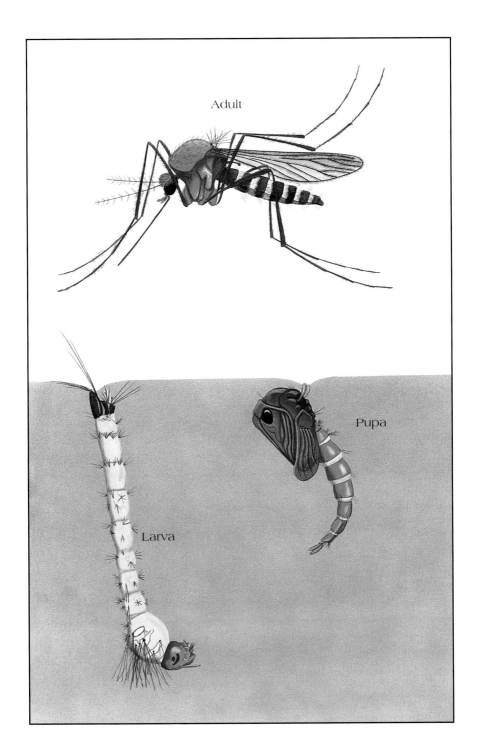

Adult

Pupa

Larva

Glossary

antennae appendages or 'feelers' on the head of an insect

callus tissue masses of cells produced by plants in response to injury

caterpillar moth or butterfly larva

chrysalis a common name referring to the pupa of a butterfly

cocoon outer protective covering around a pupa

defensive secretion a foul-smelling liquid produced by some insects when disturbed

elytra hard, outer wing cases in beetles

endemic found only in New Zealand

frass sawdust-like faecal remains

grub beetle larva

hibernate to pass winter in a dormant or lethargic condition

host the insect/animal that is used by a parasite to live on

instar the stage in the development of an insect between any two moults

larva stage between egg and pupa of those insects that undergo complete metamorphosis

maggot fly larva

metamorphosis development from egg to adult through a series of different stages

moult when one stage of a larva or nymph sheds its skin and the next stage emerges

nymph developing stage of those insects that undergo incomplete metamorphosis

ovipositor egg-laying apparatus of an adult female insect

parasite an insect/animal that lives in or on another kind of insect/animal (called its host)

predator an insect/animal that catches and eats other insects/animals (called its prey)

proboscis long mouth parts of some insects

pupa stage between larva and adult of those insects that undergo complete metamorphosis

pupate when a larva changes into a pupa

species see discussion under 'How an insect is named' (see page 15)

Further reading

Chapman, B. *Backyard Bugs: a guide to pest control in the home and garden*. Lincoln University Press, 1998.

Chapman, B and Penman, D. *The Garden Pest Book*. A.H. & A.W. Reed, 1982.

Crowe, A. *The Life-Size Guide to Insects and other Land Invertebrates of New Zealand*. Penguin Books (NZ) Ltd, 1999.

CSIRO, Division of Entomology. *The Insects of Australia*. (second edition) Melbourne University Press, 1991.

Dale, P. *A Houseful of Strangers: living with the common creatures of the New Zealand house and garden*. HarperCollins, 1992.

Forster, R.R. and Forster, L.M. *Small Land Animals of New Zealand*. John McIndoe Ltd, 1970.

Gaskin, D.E. *The Butterflies and Common Moths of New Zealand*. Whitcombe & Tombs, 1966.

Gibbs, G.W. *New Zealand Butterflies Identification and Natural History*. Collins, 1980.
The Monarch Butterfly. Reed Publishing (NZ) Ltd, 1994.
New Zealand Weta. Reed Publishing (NZ) Ltd, 1998.

Grant, E.A. *An Illustrated Guide to some New Zealand Insect Families*. Manaaki Whenua Press, 1999.

Landcare Research NZ Ltd. *Fauna of New Zealand*. A scientific series of refereed occasional publications. Manaaki Whenua Press.

Marsh, N. *Trout Stream Insects of New Zealand: How to imitate and use them*. Millwood Press, 1983.

Miller, D. (revised and edited by Annette K. Walker) *Common Insects in New Zealand*. A.H. & A.W. Reed, 1984.

New Zealand Entomological Society Bulletins *Guide to Aquatic Insects of New Zealand*, (revised edition), No. 9, 1989.
Bibliography of New Zealand terrestrial invertebrates, 1771–1985, and guide to the database BUGS, No. 11, 1992.
Handbook of New Zealand Names. Common and Scientific Names for Insects and Allied Organisms, No. 12, 1999.

Orr, M. *Those Sandflies: what they are, why they bite, and what you can do about them*. Cape Catley, Ltd, 1996.

Parkinson, B. *Butterflies and Moths of New Zealand*. Reed Publishing (NZ) Ltd, 2000.

Sharell, R. *New Zealand Insects and their Story*. Collins, 1971.

Walker, A.K. and Crosby, T.K. (revised edition) *The Preparation and Curation Insects*. DSIR Information Series 163, 1988.

Index of common names

Index of scientific names